STATISTICAL
MECHANICAL
ANALOGIES

PRENTICE-HALL SERIES IN MATERIALS SCIENCE

John Dorn, editor

ELECTRONIC AND MAGNETIC BEHAVIOR OF MATERIALS

Allen Nussbaum

INTRODUCTION TO STRENGTHENING MECHANISMS

David K. Felbeck

ORGANIC POLYMERS

Turner Alfrey and Edward F. Gurnee

QUANTUM MECHANICS FOR SCIENCE AND ENGINEERING

Herbert A. Pohl

STATISTICAL MECHANICAL ANALOGIES

Dan McLachlan, Jr.

STATISTICAL MECHANICAL ANALOGIES

Dan McLachlan, Jr.

Professor, Department of Mineralogy
Ohio State University

Prentice-Hall, Inc., Englewood Cliffs, New Jersey

Current printing (last digit):
10 9 8 7 6 5 4 3 2 1

Library of Congress Catalog Card Number 67-29361

Printed in the United States of America

Prentice-Hall International, Inc., *London*
Prentice-Hall of Australia, Pty. Ltd., *Sydney*
Prentice-Hall of Canada, Ltd., *Toronto*
Prentice-Hall of India Private Ltd., *New Delhi*
Prentice-Hall of Japan, Inc., *Tokyo*

To
Henry Eyring

PREFACE

The writing of this book was inspired by observations over many years that students, who are forced to jump from the usual course in physical chemistry in their junior or senior years to statistical mechanics in their first year of graduate school, undergo quite a bit of inconvenience by not having an adequate background in probability theory and other related subjects. Student advisors in graduate school are reluctant to send their students to the mathematics departments to get a full course in the various related subjects, because only a small fraction of what the students learn in these fine courses is ever applied back in the chemistry department (or in the departments of metallurgy or ceramics, etc.). What a student needs to get started is a brief introduction to the minimum background necessary to start, with confidence, the first course in statistical mechanics. There was a time when it was debated among curricula planners as to which should be taken first, statistical mechanics or quantum mechanics, but a more recent trend is to combine the two subjects into the same course and to weave them into thermodynamics.

The above remarks regarding the students' needs largely describe the purpose of this small book. Ronald W. Gurney (see Ref. 16) and G. S. Rushbrooke (Ref. 32) are notable among authors who have done much to get the subject expressed clearly and in a sequence that a beginning student can grasp, and B. A. Moelwyn-Hughes (Ref. 26) has supplied numerical examples and tables to give the student ideas about the sizes of the numbers involved; but although these authors and others have been "leaned upon" to help in the present book, it is intended to be more elementary than any of them. It is intended that this book should help the student about as far as the fifth page of each chapter in the advanced texts such as the book by Eyring, Henderson, Stover, and Eyring (Ref. 10).

It is almost unnecessary to say that in a book of this brevity, there are many important subjects left out, such as the grand partition function, chemical potential, and reaction rate theory.

The author is indebted to Dr. John G. Aston, who in 1935 conducted a semester seminar in statistical mechanics at Pennsylvania State University at a time when not all land-grant colleges had gotten around to introducing a subject so advanced in chemistry departments. Great benefit was also enjoyed by the author in being able to sit in on Dr. Henry Eyring's excellent lectures at the University of Utah in 1947 and 1948. The author must also acknowledge the help derived from reading the writings of a number of authors; for this reason, the list of references is placed at the beginning of the book, not only to make their names closely associated with the acknowledgements, but also to make them more accessible to the reader than they would be at the back of the book.

The author is also greatly indebted to Dr. John E. Dorn of Berkeley, Dr. John F. G. Hicks of Columbus, Ohio, William Band of Washington State University, Robert R. Reeber of Ohio State University, and Felix T. Smith of the Stanford Research Institute for reading the manuscript and giving valuable suggestions.

D. McL.

CONTENTS

REFERENCES

1. William P. Allis and Melvin A. Herlin, *Thermodynamics and Statistical Mechanics*. New York: McGraw-Hill Book Company (1952).

2. William A. Band, *Quantum Statistics*. Princeton, N. J.; D. Van Nostrand (1955).

3. R. B. Barnes, R. C. Gore, Urner Liddel, and Van Zant Williams, *Infrared Spectroscopy (Industrial Applications and Bibliography)*. New York: Reinhold Publishing Company (1944).

4. Henry A. Bent, *The Second Law*. New York and London: Oxford Press (1965).

5. Leon Brillouin, *Science and Information Theory*. New York: Academic Press (1963).

6. William Elwood Byerley, *Fourier Series and Spherical Cylindrical and Elliptical Harmonics*. Boston: Ginn and Company (1893).

7. L. S. Darken and R. W. Gurry, *Physical Chemistry of Metals*. New York: McGraw-Hill Book Company (1953).

8. Kenneth Denbigh, *The Principles of Chemical Equilibrium*. Cambridge University Press (1964).

9. E. W. Elcock, *Order-Disorder Phenomena*. New York: John Wiley & Sons (1956).

10. Henry Eyring, Douglas Henderson, Betty Jones Stover, and Edward M. Eyring, *Statistical Mechanics and Dynamics.* New York: John Wiley & Sons (1964).

11. Alfred W. Francis, *Liquid-Liquid Equilibrium.* New York and London: Interscience Publishers (1963).

12. J. D. Fast, *Entropy.* New York: McGraw-Hill Book Company (1962).

13. Thornton C. Fry, *Probability and its Engineering Uses.* Princeton, N. J.: D. Van Nostrand (1920).

14. Fredrick H. Getman, *Outlines of Theoretical Chemistry.* New York: John Wiley & Sons (1928).

15. H. S. Green and C. A. Hurst, *Order-Disorder Phenomena.* London and New York: Interscience Publishers (1964).

16. Ronald W. Gurney, *Introduction to Statistical Mechanics.* New York: McGraw-Hill Book Company (1949).

17. Max Hansen, *Constitution of Binary Alloys,* 2nd ed. New York: McGraw-Hill Book Company (1958) [In English].

18. Gerhard Herzberg, *Spectra of Diatomic Molecules.* Princeton, N. J.: D. Van Nostrand (1950).

19. Gerhard Herzberg, *Infrared and Ramon Spectra.* Princeton, N. J.: D. Van Nostrand (1945).

20. L. D. Landau and E. M. Lifshitz, translated by E. Peierls and R. F. Peierls, *Statistical Physics.* Oxford: Pergamon Press; and Reading, Mass.: Addison-Wesley Publishing Company (1958).

21. R. T. Lansberg, *Thermodynamics With Quantum Statistical Illustrations.* New York: Interscience Publishers (1961).

22. E. M. Levin, C. R. Robbins, and H. F. McMurdie, *Phase Diagrams for Ceramists.* American Ceramic Society, Inc. (1964).

23. Robert Bruce Lindsay, *Physical Statistics.* New York: John Wiley & Sons (1941).

24. John Lumsden, *Thermodynamics of Alloys*. The Institute of Metals, 4 Grosvenor Gardens, London S. W. 1 (1952).

25. J. E. Mayer and M. G. Mayer, *Statistical Mechanics*. New York: John Wiley & Sons (1946).

26. E. A. Moelwyn-Hughes, *Physical Chemistry* (an introduction). Cambridge University Press (1951).

27. A. N. Nesmeyanov (edited by Robert Gary), *Vapor Pressures of the Chemical Elements*. Amsterdam and New York: Elsevier Publishing Company (1963).

28. Linus Pauling and E. Bright Wilson, *Introduction to Quantum Mechanics*. New York: McGraw-Hill Book Company (1935).

29. B. O. Peirce and R. M. Foster, *A Short Table of Integrals,* 4th ed. Boston: Ginn and Company (1956).

30. John E. Ricci, *The Phase Rule and Heterogeneous Equilibrium*. Princeton, N. J.: D. Van Nostrand (1951).

31. F. K. Richtmyer, *Introduction to Modern Physics*. New York: McGraw-Hill Book Company (1928).

32. G. S. Rushbrooke, *Statistical Mechanics*. Oxford: Clarendon Press (1964).

33. John C. Slater, *Introduction to Chemical Physics*. New York: McGraw-Hill Book Company (1939).

34. Colin J. Smithells, *Metals Reference Book*. London: Butterworths Scientific Publications (1955).

35. Myron Tribus, *Thermodynamics and Thermostatics*. Princeton, N. J.: D. Van Nostrand (1961).

36. E. Bright Wilson, J. C. Decius and Paul C. Cross, *Molecular Vibrations*. New York: McGraw-Hill Book Company (1955).

37. Ta-Yau Wu, *Vibrational Spectra and Structure of Polyatomic Molecules*. Jum-Ming, China: National University of Peking (1939).

STATISTICAL
MECHANICAL
ANALOGIES

COINS
AND SANDBOXES

Introduction

If one had a bottle containing 22,400 cubic centimeters of helium gas at zero degrees centigrade and at a pressure of one atmosphere, it would have 6.02×10^{23} atoms of helium in it. This is a very large number. Also these atoms are traveling with an average velocity of about four thousand miles per hour.* But these atoms do not all travel with this *average* velocity; they have a distribution of velocities varying from several thousand times the average velocity down to almost zero, and the direction of their movements is in all possible directions. They collide with the walls and with one another. Helium is the simplest of all gases; other less perfect gases have a tendency for some of the atoms to go about in pairs, which rotate and vibrate, and in addition to this some of the pairs get torn apart in their collisions and some pairs momentarily stick or adhere to one another making larger aggregates.

For hundreds of years scientists have sought for laws governing the behavior of complex systems such as helium gas and other more complicated gases, liquids, and solids. The beginning was made through the efforts of such men as Boyle, Berthollet, Gay-Lussac, Avogadro, and many others by careful experimentation in which the variables, T, P, V, were observed and the relationships between them were established. Later thermodynamics came to the aid of experimenters.

*The average velocity of the molecules in the air we breathe is about 750 miles per hour.

These initial workers did not make much use of Newton's laws of motion for free translation of ponderable bodies (such as atoms) or of the law of action and reaction upon the collision of spheres until the kinetic theories of gases were developed. Even with kinetic theory, the behavior of a gas as an aggregate of many billions of atoms could not be accounted for by a minute computation of the motions of each single atom and of its interactions with those with which it came in contact. Under the general subject "statistical mechanics" a new approach to the problem has been devised. This new approach has for its underlying core the theory of probability.

If two men are gambling, it is difficult or impossible to predict the outcome of any single game even when the odds are known, but if the games are repeated often enough the over-all outcome becomes increasingly certain. Although the insurance companies cannot predict when a single individual will die, they can be pretty accurate in predicting how many people will die next year in a town of one hundred thousand. And for much the same reasons that one can predict the behavior of a swarm of bees over a period of a year much more accurately than one can predict the behavior of a single bee tomorrow, so also by statistical mechanics one can compute the properties of a volume of 10^{23} gas atoms (or molecules) much better than that of a single atom. So the theory of probability is the basis of many predictions in games, mortality data, agriculture, and thermodynamics; the simplest of all problems involving probability is that of the tossing of coins.

1-1 The Tossing of Coins

Perhaps the simplest problems in the theory of probability* are to be illustrated by the tossing of coins. We can define a "coin" in a broad sense for the present purposes as any object with two or more sides, some of which are distinguishable. See Fig. 1-1(a-e).

1-2 The Two-Sided Unloaded Coin

The simplest of all coins is the coin that has two sides which are distinguishable, Fig. 1-1(b). We will designate the sides by the numbers 1 and 2 or by the words heads and tails. By "unloaded" we mean

*One of the most stimulating discussions of various aspects of probability for the beginner is furnished by Fry, Ref. 13.

that when the coin is tossed either side is equally likely to come up. This equal likelihood has to be established by experience of many trials, as will be demonstrated later. The term "loaded" is borrowed from the jargon of the gamblers with dice, i.e., "crapshooters," to

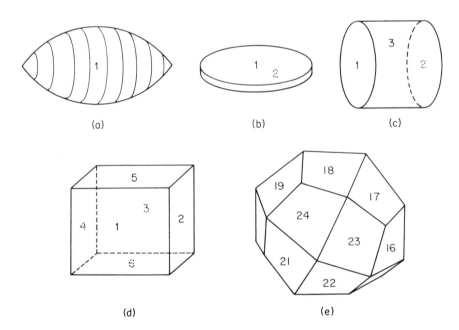

(a)　　　　　　　　　(b)　　　　　　　　　(c)

(d)　　　　　　　　　(e)

FIGURE 1-1　Some special "coins." (a) The football-shaped figure with just one number on it corresponds to a one-sided coin. (b) The usual two-sided coin. (c) A three-sided coin, which is really an ordinary coin thick enough to have a finite probability of falling on edge. It is "unloaded" if the shape is so adjusted that each of the numbers 1, 2, and 3 are equally likely to appear. (d) The six-sided coin, or die. (e) A 24-sided regular polyhedron.

indicate that a weight is introduced inside the die to increase the probability of certain numbers such as 2 or 5 to come up; consequently, each of the six sides is not equally likely to show one-sixth of the time.

When 1 comes up on a throw of a coin, that is an event, and when 2 comes up, that is a separate event. Thus there are two possible events upon the throw of a coin of this kind. Since the numbers 1 and 2 cannot come up simultaneously on a single throw, the events are said to be "mutually exclusive." This definition is unnecessary in this particularly trivial case, but it might be needed later.

1-3   A Priori Probability

The fact the two sides are equally likely to come up means that the chance that a 1 shows after a single throw is $\frac{1}{2}$ and that a 2 shows is $\frac{1}{2}$. The quantity (always a fraction) stating the probability of an event's happening among other possible events is called the "a priori probability" and is indicated by a lower case letter p with a subscript such as i or j to designate the serial number of the event. In our case the a priori probabilities are p_1 and p_2. Since the coin is not loaded,

$$p_1 = p_2 = \tfrac{1}{2} \tag{1-1}$$

and

$$p_1 + p_2 = 1 \tag{1-1a}$$

When considering an unloaded die, we can consider it to be a six-sided coin with j running from 1 to 6 and

$$p_1 + p_2 + p_3 + p_4 + p_5 + p_6 = 1$$

1-4   Unequal A Priori Probabilities

In a loaded coin with two sides [see Fig. 1–2(a)], p_1 and p_2 might not each equal $\frac{1}{2}$. They might be so unbalanced that $p_1 = \frac{1}{3}$ and $p_2 = \frac{2}{3}$. But in any case Eq. 1–1(a) must be obeyed; the sum of the a priori probabilities must be unity, as

$$p_1 + p_2 = \tfrac{1}{3} + \tfrac{2}{3} = 1$$

When a many-sided coin is considered, so that any one of many events can occur, then

$$p_1 + p_2 \cdots p_j \cdots p_L = 1 \tag{1-2}$$

where L is the number of sides on the coin, or, more briefly,

$$\sum_{j=1}^{j=L} p_j = 1 \tag{1-2a}$$

The symbol $\sum$ in Eq. 1–2(a) means addition as performed in Eq. 1–2, and the serial number j runs from 1 to L.

1-5   The Number of Ways W

In studying probability, one is frequently concerned with the "number of ways" in which a specified set of events can happen in a group of events. We will show what we mean by a set of events by illustrating with two or more throws of a penny. For example, if we were to throw the same penny twice, we could get the following results, of which there are four:

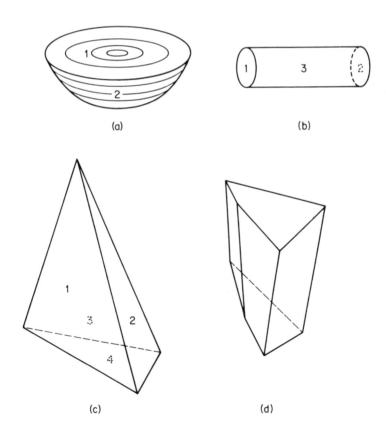

(a)

(b)

(c)

(d)

FIGURE 1-2   "Coins" that are "loaded" because of their shapes. (a) A two-sided coin with great difference in chances of the two sides coming up on a throw. (b) A cylinder representing a three-sided coin. (c) An irregular tetrahedron. (d) An irregular six-sided figure.

On the first throw we could get heads or tails. On the second throw after getting heads we could get heads or tails, and on the second throw after getting tails we could get heads or tails. The table form is shown in Table 1-1.

Table 1-1   The possible results of two throws

First Throw	Second Throw		
heads ———————	{ heads	{ 1	1
	{ tails	{ 1	2
or		or	
tails ———————	{ heads	{ 2	1
	{ tails	{ 2	2

There are four possible outcomes or ways that a penny can exhibit heads and tails on two throws (although only one of these ways can come about on just two throws). In this case we will write

$$W_2 = 2^2 = 4 \qquad (1-3)$$

for reasons which will become clear later. In Table 1–1, last column, we have shown the results by numerals for brevity instead of the words "head" and "tail."

Table 1–2 shows the possible outcomes or ways for three throws.

Table 1-2   Ways of throwing a penny three times

Throw 1	2	3		1 2 3	No.
head	head	head		1 1 1	1
head	head	tail		1 1 2	2
head	tail	head		1 2 1	3
head	tail	tail	or	1 2 2	4
tail	head	head		2 1 1	5
tail	head	tail		2 1 2	6
tail	tail	head		2 2 1	7
tail	tail	tail		2 2 2	8

The next to last column of Table 1–2 contains the numbers assigned to heads and tails as in Table 1–1, and the last column is just a serial number for each way, and it is to be noticed that there are just eight of them. We can write this for three throws as,

$$W_3 = 2^3 = 8 \qquad (1-4)$$

If one were to continue this line of reasoning indefinitely for an arbitrary number of throws n, with a two-sided coin such as a penny, one could show that

$$W_n = 2^n \qquad (1-5)$$

and for a three-sided coin

$$W_n = 3^n \qquad\qquad (1\text{-}6)$$

and for a six-sided coin or die

$$W_n = 6^n \qquad\qquad (1\text{-}7)$$

For an L-sided coin

$$W_n = L^n \qquad\qquad (1\text{-}8)$$

1-6 Restrictions on the Ways

It is worthwhile to note that the numbers of possible ways that a set of events can occur (as displayed in Eqs. 1–3 to 1–8) are not a function of the a priori probabilities.

Now let us consider a *restricted* number of ways that a group of events can happen as contrasted to the *total* number of ways we have just computed. Let us ask how many ways there are in Table 1–1 of getting two heads in two throws. From the table we can see that there is just one way. There are two ways of getting one head and one tail, and only one way of getting two tails. These results can be tabulated as follows:

$$W(11) = 1 \qquad\qquad (1\text{-}9a)$$
$$W(12) = 2 \qquad\qquad (1\text{-}9b)$$
$$W(22) = 1 \qquad\qquad (1\text{-}9c)$$

The numbers inserted in parentheses after the W's disregard the sequence of occurrence of the events. The sum of the ways

$$W(11) + W(12) + W(22) = 1 + 2 + 1 = 4$$

agrees with Eq. (1–3).

Inspection of Table 1–2 shows that

$$W(111) = 1 \qquad\qquad (1\text{-}10a)$$
$$W(112) = 3 \qquad\qquad (1\text{-}10b)$$
$$W(122) = 3 \qquad\qquad (1\text{-}10c)$$
$$W(222) = 1 \qquad\qquad (1\text{-}10d)$$

If we add the answers in Eqs. 1–10(a–d) we get 8, as found in Eq. 1–4. So we see that the answer to the question of how many ways there are of getting two heads and one tail in three throws of a penny is, according to Eq. 1–10(b), a number less than 8 but more than the ways of getting three heads. So $W(112)$ is less restricted than W_3 or $W(111)$.

In such a logical process there should be a general equation which will give the answers to Eqs. 1–9(a–c). Let us first inspect the equation that others have given us and then explain it later. The equation* is

$$W(n_1 n_2) = \frac{n!}{n_1! \, n_2!} \tag{1-11}$$

where $n!$ means $n(n-1)(n-2)(n-3) \cdots (n-n+1)$. For example, $2! = 2 \times 1$, $3! = 3 \times 2 \times 1 = 6$, $4! = 4 \times 3 \times 2 \times 1 = 24$, etc. Table 1–10, showing these products, called "factorials," is at the end of this chapter. In Eq. 1–11, n is the number of throws of the penny, n_1 is the number of heads and n_2 is the number of tails. Let us use Eq. 1–11 to get the answers in Eqs. 1–10(a–d).

$$(1\text{--}10a) \qquad W(111) = W(30) = \frac{3!}{3! \, 0!} = 1$$

$$(1\text{--}10b) \qquad W(112) = W(21) = \frac{3!}{2! \, 1!} = 3$$

$$(1\text{--}10c) \qquad W(122) = W(12) = \frac{3!}{1! \, 2!} = 3 \tag{1-12}$$

$$(1\text{--}10d) \qquad W(222) = W(03) = \frac{3!}{0! \, 3!} = 1$$

For Table 1–1 and Eqs. 1–19(a–c) we use Eq. 1–11 with $n = 2$. For a three-sided coin we must use the equation

$$W(n_1 n_2 n_3) = \frac{n!}{n_1! \, n_2! \, n_3!} \tag{1-13}$$

For an L-sided coin we use the equation

$$W(n_1 n_2 \cdots n_j \cdots n_L) = \frac{n!}{n_1! \, n_2! \cdots n_L!} \tag{1-14}$$

Now we introduce a new symbol Π, which is as frequently encountered in this work as is the summation sign Σ introduced in Eq. 1–2(a). Whereas the Σ means addition of a series, Π means the multiplication of a series; thus

$$a_1 \times a_2 \times a_3 \cdots a_j \cdots a_L \equiv \prod_{j=1}^{j=L} a_j$$

So Eq. 1–14 can be shortened to

$$W(n_1 \cdots n_j \cdots n_L) = \frac{n!}{\prod\limits_{j=1}^{L} (n_j!)} \tag{1-15}$$

*A number of useful equations for combinatory problems are given in Ref. 25, pp. 435–438.

1-7 Permutations

Equations 1–11, 1–12, and 1–13 can be justified by thinking about permutations. Permutations have to do with the ways that distinguishable objects can be arranged in sequence. Let us take three letters of our alphabet—say *a*, *b*, and *c*. They can be arranged in the following ways:

$$abc \quad bac \quad cab$$
$$acb \quad bca \quad cba$$

Note that there are six ways. Of the three letters, any one can be taken first; then for each of these three any two of the remainder can be taken, and finally one is left. So the ways are

$$W_3 = 3 \times 2 \times 1 = n! = 6 \tag{1-16}$$

The arrangement of the four letters *a*, *b*, *c*, and *d* is shown in Table 1–3. In this case we have 24 ways, because we have four choices for

Table 1-3   THE PERMUTATION OF FOUR LETTERS

abcd	bacd	cabd	dabc
abdc	badc	cadb	dacb
acbd	bcad	cbad	dbac
acdb	bcda	cbda	dbca
adbc	bdac	cdab	dcab
adcb	bdca	cdba	dcba

the first letter, three for the second choice, two for the third and the remaining letter to take last. So in the permutation of four letters we have

$$W_4 = 4 \times 3 \times 2 \times 1 = 4! = 24 \tag{1-17}$$

We now can accept the thought that the number of ways that η mutually exclusive events can happen is $\eta!$. When dealing with the tosses of a coin where all sides are different or arranging letters that are different, one is dealing with mutually exclusive events. But there are two ways that the events can become not mutually exclusive: (1) the coin can be tossed more than once, or (2) the coin can have some sides with the same numbers on them (leading to an alteration in a priori probability). Let us consider the last one first.

Suppose that in the above illustration of four letters, two or more of the letters were indistinguishable. For example, suppose for simplicity that there are two *a*'s but no *b*. Then the distinguishable arrangements are shown in Table 1–4.

Table 1-4 THE PERMUTATION OF FOUR LETTERS
WHEN TWO ARE ALIKE

a a c d	*a d c a*
a a d c	*d a c a*
a d a c	*c a a d*
d a a c	*c a d a*
a c a d	*c d a a*
a c d a	*d c a a*

There are only 12 of these arrangements. The reason for the number 12 instead of 24 is that by assigning $b = a$, we lost the permutations of two letters (a and b), which divides the product in Eq. 1–17 by a W_2 which applies to two objects being permuted,

$$W_2 = 2! = 2$$

The distinguishable ways of permuting four letters when two are alike is then

$$W = \frac{W_4}{W_2} = \frac{4!}{2!} = \frac{24}{2} = 12 \qquad (1\text{–}18)$$

To get back to coins, let us consider a regular tetrahedron as a four-sided "coin" with the numbers 1, 2, 3, and 4 marked on the faces. There are several ways or sequences in which the coin may fall, just as there are several ways of arranging the four letters a, b, c, and d. If it is thrown so that any one of the four numbers is on the table first, there are three ways for the second throw, two for the third, and one remaining, making in all $4 \times 3 \times 2 \times 1 = 4! = 24$ ways of throwing the tetrahedral coin in four throws. If two of the numerals on the coin were identical, say 2 and 3, then we would have the numbers 1 2 2 4 to be permuted, and as before 2! would come in as a reduction factor so that

$$W = \frac{4!}{2!} = \frac{24}{2} = 12 \qquad (1\text{–}19)$$

which is the same as Eq. 1–18.

The important aspect of identical sides on coins or identical letters in a word group is that the a priori probability is governed by it. If a coin has ν_1 sides of one kind, ν_2 of the second kind, and so on up to ν_K sides of the Kth kind, then the a priori probabilities are

$$p_1 = \frac{\nu_1}{L}, \, p_2 = \frac{\nu_2}{L}, \, \cdots, p_K = \frac{\nu_K}{L} \qquad (1\text{–}19a)$$

or in general

$$p_j = \frac{v_j}{L}$$

where, as before (and always), $\Sigma\, p_j = 1$. To avoid confusion, we repeat that L is the number of sides on the coin, v_j is the number of sides of the jth kind, and in addition we say

$$\sum_i^K v_j = L$$

From this we can see that in Table 1–3 the a priori probabilities are $\frac{1}{4}$ and $K = 4$, whereas in Table 1–4 the a priori probabilities are $P_a = \frac{1}{2}$, $P_b = \frac{1}{4}$, $P_c = \frac{1}{4}$, and $K = 3$, so that

$$\sum_{j=1}^{3} p_j = \tfrac{1}{2} + \tfrac{1}{4} + \tfrac{1}{4} = 1 \qquad\qquad (1\text{--}19\text{b})$$

Here we must bark a warning. Notice that Eq. 1–19(b) does not agree with Eq. 1–2(a). One of them sums up to L, the number of *sides* of the coin, and the other sums over the number of different *kinds* of sides. The latter equation is correct in general, whereas the first is correct only if the number of kinds is equal to the number of sides, as it was when we were considering Eq. 1–2(a).

Now let us examine the second way by which events can become not mutually exclusive. Although two or more 1's or 2's, etc. do not appear simultaneously on a single throw of a six-sided coin, 1 or some other number can appear more than once if three such coins are thrown simultaneously. The easiest way to compute the ways W is first to assume that there are 3! ways to share between the sides any combination which appears on the three dies. If we stipulate that two be alike we have asked for a duplication, and the ways must be divided by 2!. In general, the ways of throwing N times an L-sided coin to get N_1 sides up of the first kind, N_2 sides up of the second kind, and so on, is

$$W = \frac{n!}{n_1!\, n_2!\, n_3! \cdots} = \frac{n!}{\prod_i^L (n_j!)}$$

if the sides are all different, but if some of the sides are not different, we sum over the *kinds* of sides up to K.

$$W = \frac{n!}{\prod_i^K (n_j!)} \qquad\qquad (1\text{--}19\text{c})$$

We notice that in Eq. 1–19(c), the a priori probabilities do not appear, but the existence of differing p's does alter the limit K to which the product Π is applied.

1-8   Probability

We are now ready to illustrate a simple problem in probability. If by Eq. 1–4 there are eight ways for heads and tails to come up in three throws of a coin, and if there are only three ways, according to Eqs. 1–10(b) and 1–12, of getting two heads and one tail, then one might expect that the probability of getting two heads and one tail in three throws of the coin should be the ratio of the ways

$$P(21) = \frac{W(21)}{W(n)} = \frac{3}{8} \tag{1–20}$$

and from Table 1–2,

$$P(30) = \tfrac{1}{8}, \qquad P(03) = \tfrac{1}{8}, \quad \text{and} \quad P(12) = \tfrac{3}{8} = P(21)$$

The sum is

$$P(30) + P(03) + P(12) + P(21) = \tfrac{1}{8} + \tfrac{1}{8} + \tfrac{3}{8} + \tfrac{3}{8} = 1$$

This illustrates the principle that the sum of the separate probabilities must add up to unity, just as do the a priori probabilities in Eqs. 1–2 and 1–2(a).

Combining Eqs. 1–5 and 1–11 in the above manner gives us the probability of getting n_1 heads and n_2 tails in n throws of a two-sided coin.

$$P(n_1 n_2 n) = \frac{W(n_1 n_2)}{W(n)} = \frac{n!}{n_1! \, n_2!} \frac{1}{2^n} \tag{1–21}$$

Intuitively we can write the equation for the N throws of an L-sided coin to express the probability of getting the first side N_1 times, the second side N_2 times, and so on. We combine Eqs. 1–9 and 1–16 to get

$$P(n_1 n_2 \cdots n_L) = \frac{W(n_1 n_2 \cdots n_L)}{W(n)} = \frac{n!}{\prod\limits_{j=1}^{L} (n_j!)} \frac{1}{L^n} \tag{1–22}$$

We must remember that Eq. 1–22 applies only to those cases where the a priori probabilities are alike, i.e., $P_j = 1/L$ for all j's.

1-9   Some Properties of the Probability Equations

Looking at Table 1–2, we see that the number of times that 1 appears in the next to last column is just twelve, the same number of times that 2 appears. This agrees with our intuition that if the a priori probability is $\tfrac{1}{2}$ for both heads and tails, then in a large number of throws, the number of appearances of heads and tails should be about equal, i.e., $n/2$. Let us use Eq. 1–21 to see what the probability is for getting $n/2$ tails and $n/2$ heads. Letting $n_1 = n_2 = n/2$ in Eq. 1–21 gives

$$P\left(\frac{n}{2}\,\frac{n}{2}\,n\right) = \frac{n!}{\frac{n}{2}!\,\frac{n}{2}!}\,\frac{1}{2^n} \tag{1-23}$$

Then to comply with the conditions of Table 1–2 we let $n = 3$ in Eq. 1–23.

$$P\left(\frac{n}{2}\,\frac{n}{2}\,n\right) = P\left(\frac{3}{2}\,\frac{3}{2}\,3\right) = \frac{3!}{\left(\frac{3}{2}\right)!\left(\frac{3}{2}\right)!}\,\frac{1}{2^3} = \frac{3!}{\left[\left(\frac{3}{2}\right)!\right]^2}\,\frac{1}{2^3}$$

Since $\left(\frac{3}{2}\right)!$ is about 1.33*

$$P = \frac{6}{(1.33)^2}\,\frac{1}{8} = 0.425 \tag{1-24}$$

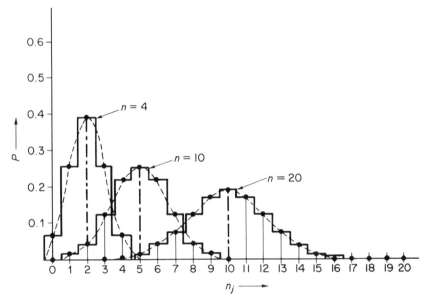

FIGURE 1-3 Histogram of the data shown in Table 1-5, showing the probabilities $P(n_1\,n_2)$ against n_j for $n = 4$, 10, and 20. Note that the figures are symmetrical about $n_j = n/2$ and that the dotted lines resemble "bell curves." Also, the areas under these curves are all the same, i.e., there is unity.

Notice that P in Eq. 1–24 is less than $\frac{1}{2}$. If all values of n_1 and n_2 were used in Eq. 1–21, we expect that the corresponding probabilities would be less. A plot to show graphically how the probabilities vary

*For a discussion of factorials of nonintegers, see Ref. 13.

as n_1 and n_2 deviate from $n/2$ would be interesting. Table 1–5 furnishes data from which such graphs can be drawn.

Histograms representing the probabilities given in Table 1–5 plotted against n_1 are shown in Fig. 1–3. It is to be noticed that the maximum probabilities are at $n_1 = n/2$ in every case, as one would expect, but the value of the maximum probability decreases as n gets larger.

Table 1-5 SOLVING FOR PROBABILITIES USING EQ. (1-21)

n	n_1	n_2	$w(n_1n_2)$	$w = 2^n$	$P(n_1n_2)$
2	2	0	1	4	0.25
	1	1	2		0.50
	0	2	1		0.25
3	3	0	1	8	0.125
	2	1	3		0.375
	1	2	3		0.375
	0	3	1		0.125
4	4	0	1	16	0.0625
	3	1	4		0.25
	2	2	6		0.375
	1	3	4		0.25
	0	4	1		0.0625
10	10	0	1	1024	0.001
	9	1	10		0.01
	8	2	45		0.044
	7	3	120		0.117
	6	4	210		0.204
	5	5	252		0.246
	4	6	210		0.204
	3	7	120		0.117
	2	8	45		0.044
	1	9	10		0.01
	0	10	1		0.001
20	20	0	1	1,046,576	0
	19	1	20		2×10^{-5}
	18	2	190		1.88×10^{-4}
	17	3	1140		1.08×10^{-3}
	16	4	4745		4.5×10^{-3}
	15	5	1.55×10^4		1.47×10^{-2}
	14	6	3.86×10^4		0.026
	13	7	7.76×10^4		0.074
	12	8	1.27×10^5		0.120
	11	9	1.68×10^5		0.160
	10	10	1.84×10^5		0.175

One could solve for these maximum probabilities by the use of Eq. 1–23, but in preparation for problems in which large numbers are involved (and the longhand computation of factorials is too laborious), we should stop and introduce an approximation which has been adopted by statisticians in chemistry, agricultural research, and many other fields of endeavor.

1-10   The Stirling Approximations*

Stirling presented an equation for computing factorial m, where m is any positive number.

$$m! = \sqrt{2\pi m}\; m^m e^{-m}[S] \qquad (1\text{–}25)$$

where $[S]$ is a series whose first term is unity. When $[S]$ is assigned the value unity, it gives just as accurate a value for $m!$ as one can wish for when m is large. But the use of the series is cumbersome in long derivations, and for large values of m it does not reduce much the percentage of inaccuracy. There are several stages of approximation even cruder than $S = 1$, which people find feasible, depending upon good judgment in regard to the magnitude of m. Leaving off the $[S]$ terms is the first stage. It and the other worse stages of approximation follow:

First stage:

$$m! \doteq \sqrt{2\pi m}\; m^m e^{-m} \qquad (1\text{–}26a)$$

Second stage:

$$m! = m^m e^{-m} \qquad (1\text{–}26b)$$

Third stage:

$$m! \doteq m^m \qquad (1\text{–}26c)$$

The logarithms of these approximations are (in the same order)

$$\ln m! \doteq \tfrac{1}{2} \ln 2\pi m + m \ln m - m \qquad (1\text{–}27a)$$

$$\ln m! = m \ln m - m \qquad (1\text{–}27b)$$

$$\ln m! = m \ln m \qquad (1\text{–}27c)$$

In most practical work, one most often uses either the second or the third stages of approximation.

In order to illustrate the use of these approximations, we apply them to Eq. 1–23. The first approximation of Eq. 1–23 is

*A derivation of the Stirling approximations is given in Ref. 13, pp. 103–106.

to indicate the widths of the curves at one-half the maximum height of $P(nf)_{\max} = P(N\frac{1}{2})$. It is noticeable that the "width-at-half-height" (as these curves are frequently characterized) decreases as *n* increases, in contrast to the curves shown in Fig. 1–3.

The contrast in these curves is further emphasized (see Table 1–8)

FIGURE **1-4**   The probability data of Table 1-8 plotted against n_j/n. Note that the curves are now symmetrical about the 0.5 mark, and the lines *AA'* representing the widths at half-height become shorter as *n* increases.

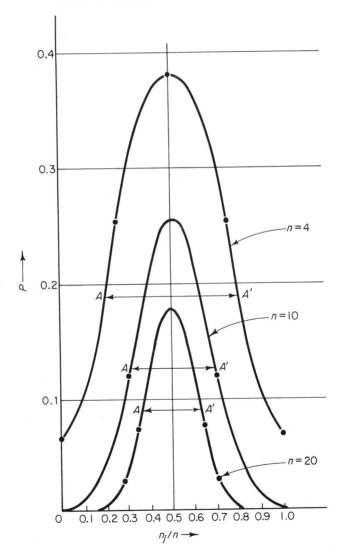

Table 1-8 $P(nf)$ Converted from Table 1-5

1	2	3	4	5
n	n_1	f	$P(nf)$	$P(nf)/P(n\frac{1}{2})$
4	4	1	0.0625	0.1665
	3	0.75	0.250	0.665
	2	0.50	0.375	1.00
	1	0.25	0.250	0.665
	0	0	0.0625	0.1665
10	10	1.0	0.001	0.00406
	9	0.9	0.01	0.0406
	8	0.8	0.044	0.18
	7	0.7	0.117	0.475
	6	0.6	0.204	0.830
	5	0.5	0.246	1.000
20	20	1.0	0.00	0.00
	19	0.95	2.0×10^{-5}	1.04×10^{-5}
	18	0.90	1.88×10^{-4}	0.00108
	17	0.85	1.08×10^{-3}	0.0067
	16	0.80	4.5×10^{-3}	0.0257
	15	0.75	1.47×10^{-2}	0.084
	14	0.70	0.026	0.148
	13	0.65	0.0737	0.421
	12	0.60	0.120	0.685
	11	0.55	0.160	0.915
	10	0.50	0.175	1.000

by plotting the ratio $P(nf)/P(n\frac{1}{2})$ as in Fig. 1–5. This brings all the curves to the same height of unity without changing the widths at half-height from what they are in Fig. 1–4.

Although we will not make use of the fact in our present work, it is of interest to know that Poisson derived an equation to express the expected deviations from expectancy.

$$P_n(n_1) = \frac{e^{-\epsilon}e^{n_1}}{n_1!} \tag{1-38}$$

where ϵ is the expected number $p_1 n$. However, this form of the probability equation will not be applied in the present work.

We are more interested in an equation due to Gauss. It appears in many forms, of which a typical one is

$$y = Ae^{-\beta x^2} \tag{1-39}$$

This gives a bell-shaped curve, since x can take on both positive and

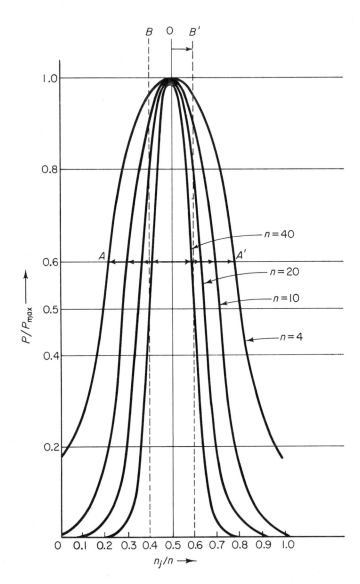

FIGURE 1-5   The data of Table 1–8 were used for this figure. Again, n_j/n is used as abscissa, causing the symmetry still to be about the dividing line at $n_j/n = 0.5$; but the ordinate being P/P_{max} causes all the curves to be the same height. Notice that the widths at half-height are the same as they are in Fig. 1–4. If a band through the center having width BB' is drawn, it almost covers the area of the curve for $n = 40$. This latter fact is closely related to the significance of Poisson's equation (Eq. 1–38).

negative values. A is the peak height of the curve and is a constant. A more common form applied by physicists is

$$y = \sqrt{\frac{2}{\pi}} \int e^{-x^2/2} \, dx \quad \text{(error function)} \quad (1\text{--}40)$$

By an adjustment of variables either Eq. 1–39 or 1–40 can be made to fit the curves in Fig. 1–3 (or Fig. 1–5). Since it is conveniently desirable to integrate from O to B' (see Fig. 1–5) to get the area under a curve from the center out to some value of X, and since Eq. 1–40 is not readily integrable, tables have been compiled and made easily available for the purpose.* The Gaussian type that we are at present interested in is one that does what Eq. 1–11 does; that is, produce the continuous curves in Fig. 1–5. The equation is

$$P(n_1 n) = \sqrt{\frac{2}{\pi n}} \, e^{-(2/n)[n_1-(n/2)]^2} \quad (1\text{--}41)$$

Notice that when $n_1 = n/2$ is inserted into this equation, the exponential term becomes unity and the peak height becomes just as was shown in Eq. 1–28. Later we wish to introduce an L-dimensional Gaussian that will apply not only to a two-sided coin but to a general L-sided coin.

1-12 The Sandbox Analogy

In order to get into large numbers quickly, let us consider the 17 boxes in Fig. 1–6(a). A uniformly random (whatever that means) shower of sand is falling into the boxes in such a manner that after a long shower involving millions of grains of sand, an equal number of grains of sand have fallen on each and every unit of area below the shower. Each of the boxes has the same area at the top opening, so the chance of a grain of sand falling into one of the boxes is equal to that for any other. We say that the a priori probability is $\frac{1}{17}$; or if there are L boxes, $p_j = 1/L$. The total number of ways that n grains of sand can fall into these 17 boxes is, according to Eq. 1–8,

$$W_n = L^n = 17^n \quad (1\text{--}42)$$

After a long time and after n becomes very large, the number to be expected in each box is

$$n_j^* = \frac{n}{L} = np_j = \frac{n}{17} \quad (1\text{--}43)$$

for all values of j from 1 to 17. If one did not know the equivalence

*See Peirce, pp. 115–119.

of the areas of the boxes, one could still determine p_j experimentally from measurements (or counts) of n_j^*.

But if the shower were stopped after a relatively short time then n would not be so large, and one could use Eq. 1–15 to compute the

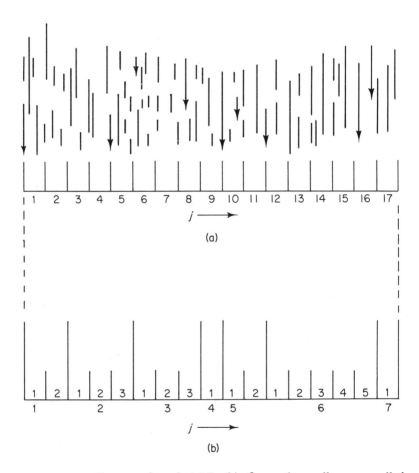

FIGURE 1-6   Showers of sand. (a) In this figure, the sandboxes are all the same size and numbered from 1 to $L = 17$; the a priori probabilities p_j are equal to 1/17. (b) In this figure, the boxes are grouped, and a new number j is assigned to each group; the a priori probabilities are not equal for all groups.

number of ways that n_1 grains fall in the first box, n_2 in the second box, and so on; one could also use Eq. 1–22 to compute the probability of this distribution's happening. We repeat Eq. 1–22 here for inspection.

$$P(n_1 \cdots n_L) = \frac{n!}{\prod\limits_{j=1}^{L}(n_j!)} \frac{1}{L^n} \tag{1-22}$$

This equation can be written so as to involve p_1 explicitly.

$$P(n_1 \cdots n_L) = \frac{n!}{\prod n_j!} p^n \tag{1-44}$$

Since $n = n_1 + n_2 + n_3 + \cdots + n_L$, Eq. 1-44 can be expanded for future comparison (when p_j is to be variable).

$$P(n_1 \cdots n_L) = \frac{n!}{\prod n_j!} p^{n_1} p^{n_2} \cdots p^{n_L} \tag{1-45a}$$

$$= \frac{n!}{\prod n_j!} p^n \tag{1-45b}$$

A more general demonstration of a priori probabilities is obtained if the partitions in Fig. 1-6(a) are removed and replaced by the partitions in Fig. 1-6(b). There are still 17 boxes in this array, but they are grouped into seven groups, the groups being numbered from $j = 1$ to $j = 7$; there are v_j boxes in each group. Now the a priori probability of a sand grain's falling into a box is still $\frac{1}{17}$ or $1/L$, but the a priori probability of a grain's falling into the group j is $P_j = v_j/17$. Looking at the figure, we see that $p_1 = \frac{2}{17}$, $p_2 = \frac{3}{17}$, $p_3 = \frac{3}{17}$, $p_4 = \frac{1}{17}$, etc. Again, if we did not know the inside arrangements and areas of the groups, we could still determine p_j from a long shower, using Eq. 1-33, $n_j^* = np_j$ or $p_j = n_j^*/n$. (Please note before it is too late that we have a new numbering system, that j has a different meaning for Figs. 4(a) and 4(b), and that n_j is to be the grains of sand, where j goes from 1 to $K = 7$ in group j.) The total number of ways that n grains of sand can fall into these groups is no longer $W_n = L^n = 1/p^n$, but is now

$$W_n = \left(\frac{1}{p_1}\right)^{n_1}\left(\frac{1}{p_2}\right)^{n_2} \cdots \left(\frac{1}{p}\right)^K = \frac{1}{\prod\limits_{j=1}^{K} p_j^{n_j}} \tag{1-46}$$

where K is the number of groups.

The probability that n_1 grains fall in the first group of boxes, n_2 in the second, and so on is

$$P(m \cdots n_K) = \frac{n!}{\prod n_j!} p_j^{n_1} p_2^{n_2} \cdots p_L^{n_L} \tag{1-47a}$$

(compare with Eq. 1-45a). More briefly,

$$P(m \cdots n_L) = \frac{n! \, \prod}{\prod n_j!} p_j^{n_j} \tag{1-47b}$$

These same equations apply when we consider a many-sided (L-sided) coin with K kinds of numerals on it; the numerals are fewer than the sides, so there are ν_j faces bearing the same numeral. Consequently, the a priori probability that the jth numeral comes up can be $p_j = \nu_j/(\text{number of faces})$, or ν_j/L.

Of course, there are other ways of getting a priori probabilities *unequal*, other than varying areas as we did with the boxes or duplicate numbers on faces of a coin or die, etc. It can also come about by energy restraints as in physical chemistry, cost restraints in business, etc.

1-13 A Geometrical Analogy*

There is a way of representing graphically the tossing of a two-sided coin, as shown in Fig. 1–7. If there are n tosses we have the condition that the sum of the number of heads and tails must equal n.

$$n_1 + n_2 = n \qquad (1\text{–}48\text{a})$$

This is analogous to the familiar equation of a straight line,

$$x + y = c \,(\text{a constant}) \qquad (1\text{–}48\text{b})$$

The only difference is that in Eq. 1–48(a) only positive integers are assumed to be appropriate, whereas Eq. 1–48(b) applies to a continuous line involving positive and negative values of x and y including fractions. In Fig. 1–7 we have laid out along the x axis the markings for the numbered integers from 1 to 10 for n_1, and along the y axis all the integers for n_2 from 1 to 10. The straight line that Eq. 1–48(a) represents is marked off as the diagonal line running from A to A' in Fig. 1–7. The rule of positive numbers assumes that in going from the origin O to the line AA' one can go only to the right and upward, as illustrated by the path (heavy line) indicated from O to the point C.

Of course, the path from O to C that is shown in Fig. 1–7 is only one of the many paths to the line AA' from O. In fact, it is only one of the many paths from O to C. The number of paths to C is evaluated by use of Eq. 1–11.

$$W(n_1 n_2) = \frac{n!}{n_1! \, n_2!} \qquad (1\text{–}11)$$

Placing $n_1 = 5$, $n_2 = 5$, and $n = 10$ in Eq. 1–11 yields 252 ways or paths. This number is recorded beyond the line AA' opposite the

*See Dan McLachlan, Jr. and L. L. Chamberlain, "Geometrical Approach to the Theory of Probability," *American Journal of Physics*, **29** (1961), 385–392.

point C in the column labeled $W(n_1 n_2)$ in the figure. These numbers for $W(n_1 n_2)$ in this column were taken directly from Table 1–5 for $n = 10$. If we add the numbers in this column we should get the grand total number of ways of traveling (positively) from the origin O to the line AA'. The actual count is 1024. Also, according to Eq. 1–5, the total number of ways should be $W_n = 2^n = 2^{10} = 1024$, agreeing with the count.

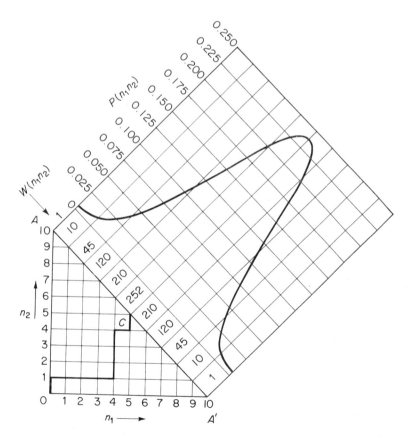

FIGURE 1-7 The random walk principle and its relation to the Gaussian curve.

The probability of starting at O and arriving at any coordinate point $n_1 n_2$ on the line AA' is computed from Eq. 1–21 and recorded for $n = 10$ in Table 1–5. These values are plotted on the auxiliary graph in Fig. 1–7, and they form a bell-shaped curve. In fact it is identical numerically to the curve for $n = 10$ in Fig. 1–3. As is seen, it is a bell curve and should agree closely with the Gaussian equation 1–41.

Figure 1–7 could also represent the random walk of a gentleman who starts at a point O with an unfailing repulsion against going south or west but stops at every street corner to decide at random whether he will try one more block east or north. If, at the end of 10 blocks of such stumbling, he drops dead, the curve in Fig. 1–7 can help as a guide in estimating the probability that the body can be found at the intersection of n_1 East Street and n_2 North Street. Most random walk problems in chemistry are not this simple.

1-14 Geometry and the Three-Sided Coin

Let us toss, n times, a coin that has three sides, where the a priori probabilities are $p_1 = p_2 = p_3 = \frac{1}{3}$. In this case sum of the n's is analogous to the equation of a plane,

$$n_1 + n_2 + n_3 = n \tag{1–49a}$$

$$x + y + z = c \text{ (a constant)} \tag{1–49b}$$

This plane is represented graphically in Fig. 1–8(a) as an equilateral triangle with corners A, B, and C where the plane intersects the x, y, and z axes. To avoid confusion, not all of the coordinate slices are shown, only the $n_1 = 1$ plane, the $n_2 = 1$ plane, and the $n_3 = 1$ plane in dotted lines. When a complete set of such planes is drawn, the face ABC becomes divided into smaller equilateral areas as are seen in Fig. 1–8(b), where $n = 20$. The reader will be reminded, by this figure, of the triangular paper used by metallurgists and ceramists in three-component equilibrium diagrams. Of course, the reason is that the sum of the percentages of their three components must add up to 100.

$$C_1 + C_2 + C_3 = 100$$

and this is the equation of a plane.

The total number of ways of going from the origin O (Fig. 1–8a) to all possible points on the plane is, by Eq. 1–6, 3^n, which is in this case 3^{20}. The number of ways of going from the point O to any particular point on the plane, $n_1 n_2 n_3$, is, by Eq. 1–13,

$$W(n_1 n_2 n_3 \, 20) = \frac{20!}{n_1! \, n_2! \, n_3!} \tag{1–50}$$

and the probability of reaching that point is

$$P(n_1 n_2 n_3 \, 20) = \frac{20!}{n_1! \, n_2! \, n_3!} \frac{1}{3^{20}} \tag{1–51}$$

Now we can imitate the researchers on equilibrium diagrams, who lay the triangular paper flat and plot out vertically the equilibrium temperatures of phase transitions. We lay the triangle ABC flat, as shown in Fig. 1–8(c), and represent probabilities by perpendiculars

FIGURE **1-8(a)** *The geometrical aspects of the three-sided coin:* The integral coordinates n_1, n_2, and n_3 with the plane whose equation is $n_1 + n_2 + n_3 = n$ (compare with Fig. 1-7).

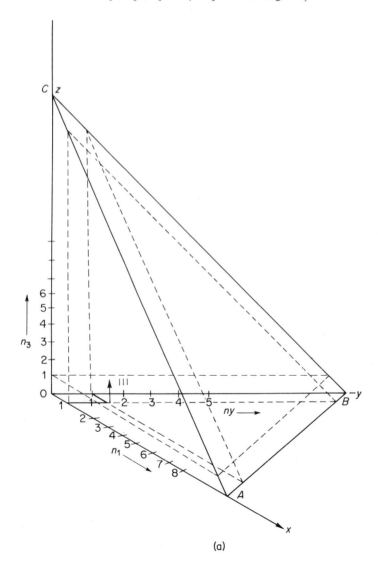

(a)

erected vertically to the plane of the page. Also, the phase-equilibrium people find that along any edge of the diagram they have only a two-component system. This is true for any line ("tie line") through the triangle. When we let $n_3 = 0$, then we are running along the edge AB of Fig. 1-8(b) and $n_1 + n_2 = 20$. Setting $n_3 = 0$ in Eq. 1-50 (and remembering $0! = 1$), we have

$$P(n_1\ n_2\ 20) = \frac{20!}{n_1!\ n_2!}\frac{1}{3^{20}} \qquad (1\text{-}52)$$

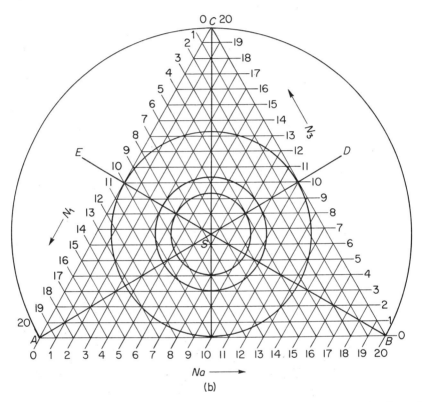

FIGURE 1-8(b) *The geometrical aspects of the three-sided coin:* The face of the plane shown in Fig. 1-8(a) with the coordinates laid out.

The results of Eq. 1-52 can be obtained from those in Table 1-5 under $n = 20$ by multiplying the factor $(2^{20}/3^{20}) = (2/3)^{20}$; the curve is shown in Fig. 1-3 except for the scale factors. This same curve is repeated schematically three times in Fig. 1-8(c) along the *A–B, B–C,* and C–A edges and perpendicular to the plane. We expect Eq. 1–51 to have a maximum value when $n_1 = n_2 = n_3 = n/3 = 6.66$, right in the center of the triangular lattice. Solving the equation

$$P(6.66, 6.66, 6.66) = \frac{20!}{(6.66)^3} \frac{1}{3^{20}} \qquad (1\text{–}52a)$$

gives the answer 0.0385.

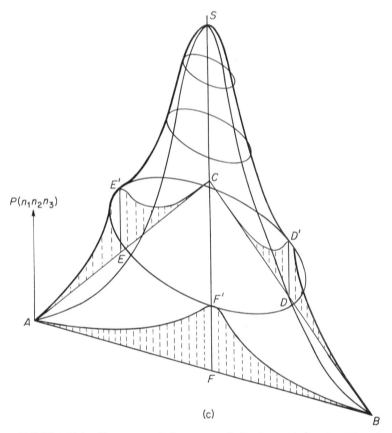

FIGURE 1-8(c) *The geometrical aspects of the three-sided coin:* The three-dimensional Gaussian "hill" with regular Gaussian boundaries.

There are three lines through the system in Fig. 1–8(b) which are of special interest. They are the lines A–D, B–E, and C–F passing through the center. Considering the line A–D, we see that this is the line along which $n_2 = n_3$ and Eq. 1–51 becomes

$$P(n_1, n_2, 20) = \frac{20!}{n_1![n_2!]^2} \frac{1}{3^{20}}$$

$$= \frac{20!}{n_1!\left[\left(\dfrac{20-n}{2}\right)!\right]^2} \frac{1}{3^{20}} \qquad (1\text{–}53)$$

Some of the results from this equation are shown in Table 1–9.

Table 1-9

n_1	$P(n_1 n_2)$	n_1	$P(n_1 n_2)$
0	6.8×10^{-5}	8	3.36×10^{-2}
2	3.4×10^{-3}	10	1.35×10^{-2}
4	1.8×10^{-2}	12	2.54×10^{-3}
6	3.82×10^{-2}	14	2.23×10^{-4}

FIGURE **1-8(d and e)** *The geometrical aspects of the three-sided coin:* (d) A plot of the data given in Table 1–9. (e) A helpful construction.

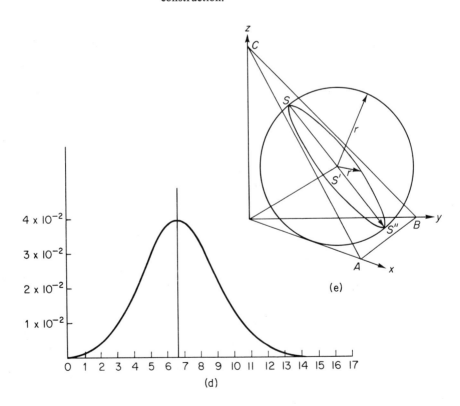

(e)

(d)

Using these data and the answer from Eq. 1–52(a), we have plotted the curve shown in Fig. 1–8(d). The curve is symmetrical about $n_1 = 6.66$, as is expected. It is obvious that the same curves would be obtained along the lines BE and CF of Fig. 1–8(b). More symmetry will become apparent later.

1-15 The K-dimensional Gaussian

In the book by Fry* and also the one by Margeneau and Murphy† there are extensions of the ordinary Gaussian to higher dimensions. We adopt the form in our symbolism as

$$P(n_1 \cdots n_k) = \frac{1}{(2\pi n)^{(K-1)/2}} \frac{1}{\left(\prod_1^K p_j\right)^{1/2}} e^{-(1/2)[(n_j - np_j)^2/2np_j]} \qquad (1\text{-}54)$$

For our problem above, we can let $K = 3$, $p_j = \frac{1}{3}$ in Eq. 1–54 to produce

$$P(n_1 n_2 n_3) = \frac{\sqrt{27}}{2\pi n} \exp\left\{-\frac{3}{4n}\left[\left(n_1 - \frac{n}{3}\right)^2 + \left(n_2 - \frac{n}{3}\right)^2 + \left(n_3 - \frac{n}{3}\right)^2\right]\right\} \qquad (1\text{-}54\text{a})$$

There are several things of interest to be done with Eq. 1–54(a). First, by letting $n_1 = n_2 = n_3 = n/3$, the exponent becomes zero, and since $e^{-0} = 1$ the equation reduces to

$$P\left(\frac{n}{3} \frac{n}{3} \frac{n}{3}\right) = \frac{\sqrt{27}}{2\pi n} = \frac{\sqrt{27}}{2\pi 20} = 0.0414$$

as compared to 0.0385 when Eq. 1–52(a) is used. The next thing we can do is to study the character of the exponent in Eq. 1–54(a). We know that when the term $[n_1 - (n/3)]^2 + [n_2 - (n/3)]^2 + [n_3 - (n/3)]^2$ does not vary (although we let n_1, n_2, and n_3 vary), the values of P also do not vary. So let us take constant values, say r^2, for this sum as follows:

$$\left(n_1 - \frac{n}{3}\right)^2 + \left(n_2 - \frac{n}{3}\right)^2 + \left(n_3 - \frac{n}{3}\right)^2 = r^2 \qquad (1\text{-}55)$$

which is analogous to the equation of a sphere of radius r located at $x_0 = a$, $y_0 = b$, $z_0 = c$.

$$(x - a)^2 + (y - b)^2 + (z - c)^2 = r^2 \qquad (1\text{-}55\text{a})$$

but $a = b = c$. Figure 1–8(e) shows the sphere drawn in the same

*Reference 13, p. 283.
†Henry Margeneau and George Mosley Murphy, *The Mathematics of Physics and Chemistry* (Princeton, N. J.: D. Van Nostrand and Co.), 1943, p. 424.

coordinate system as is shown in Fig. 1–8(a). Where this sphere of radius r intersects the plane A-B-C we get a circle of radius r on the plane. Some illustrative circles are shown on Fig. 1–8(b), and the value of $P(n_1 n_2 n_3)$ are invariant around the circumference of each of these circles or any other circle that is drawn about this same center. When a circle gets outside the triangle, that part of it must be ignored as representing negative values for some of the n_j's. These circles can be thought of as contours on the truncated hill shown in Fig. 1–8(c). The three-dimensional equi-a priori Gaussian is therefore a surface generated by the rotation, an ordinary Gaussian curve. When the a priori probabilities p_j are unequal, we get a lopsided hill, just as we get a "skewed" Gaussian in the usual case.

The reader is no doubt curious as to what the geometrical interpretation would be for a four-sided coin. This is a problem starting out with four coordinates

$$n_1 + n_2 + n_3 + n_4 = n \tag{1–56a}$$

analogous to

$$x + y + z + t = c \tag{1–56b}$$

and cannot be drawn on ordinary paper, but the "plane" which it represents is a tetrahedron* and can be drawn. The probability has no room on tablet paper to be represented perpendicular to this "plane." The probability function in the tetrahedron is a sort of a cloud with equi-density spheres (in case of equi-a priori probability) descending Gaussianlike from the center. A general interpretation of K-dimensional Gaussians involves hypertetrahedrons* and are of little interest here.

When the a priori probabilities are not equal we have equations analogous to 1–49(a) and 1–56(a), but of the from

$$v_1 n_1 + v_2 n_2 + v_3 n_3 + \cdots = n \tag{1–57}$$

These equations do not necessarily give "equilateral planes" of constant slope, as we will see when we draw the figures for $n = 2$ and 3.

PROBLEMS

1. (a) If you toss a well-balanced half dollar 100 times, how many times do you expect to get heads?

(b) If you have an urn containing an infinite number of black and

*Dan McLachlan, Jr. and L. L. Chamberlain, "Geometrical Approach to the Theory of Probability. *American Journal of Physics*, **29** (1961), 385-392.

white marbles in equal proportions and withdrew 100 of them at random how many black ones would you expect to get?

(c) If the number of black marbles in (b) above were twice the number of white marbles, how many white marbles would you expect to get in 100 draws?

(d) What are the a priori probabilities in (a), (b) and (c) above?

2. (a) If you had a die numbered in the usual way, what is the a priori probability for each of the six sides?

(b) If the six sides were renumbered so that there were 2 ones, no twos or threes, one four, no fives, and 3 sixes, what are the a priori probabilities?

(c) If you threw the die 600 times, what results would you expect?

3. (a) If you tossed the half dollar in Prob. 1(a) twice, how many combinations of heads and tails can be gotten?

(b) In Prob. 1(a), what is the probability that it would show heads both times in two tosses?

(c) What is the probability that, in two tosses of the half dollar, heads would appear at least once in two tosses?

(d) Tails at least once in two tosses?

(e) Tails and then heads in two tosses?

4. (a) By actual multiplying out, compute the values of factorial m where m runs over the integers from 1 to 10.

(b) Find the logarithm base 10 of these answers found in Prob. 4(a) and compare with those in the accompanying table.

(c) Complete Table 1–7.

5. Compute, by the following three approximations due to Stirling, the logarithms of 10, 20, 30, 40, 50, 60, 70, 80, 90, and 100:

(a) $\log M! = \dfrac{1}{2.3} \ln M_1! = \dfrac{1}{2} \log 2\pi m + m \log m - \dfrac{m}{2.3}$

(b) $\log m! = m \log m - m$

(c) $\log m! = m \log m$

(d) Compare the values in (a), (b), and (c) with those in Table 1–10(b).

6. (a) Plot curves of $\log M!$ against $M!$ as obtained in Prob. 5(a), (b), and (c).

(b) Also plot on the same paper the corresponding data from the accompanying table.

7. (a) Using $M = 10^2$, 10^4, 10^{10}, and 10^{20}, compute log $M!$ for each of the equations:

$$\log M! = m \log m - \frac{m}{2.3}$$

$$\log M! = m \log m$$

(b) At what value of m does the second equation become less than 1 per cent in error?

8. (a) In the urn problem of 1(b) what is the probability of getting 40 black and 60 white marbles in 100 draws?

(b) In the urn problem in 1(c) what is the probability of drawing 50 black marbles and 50 white marbles?

(c) What is the probability of drawing 66 black marbles and 34 white marbles?

9. Compute and draw, following Prob. 1(b), a curve of probability against M_1 the number of white marbles and $(100 - n_1)$ black marbles in 100 draws.

10. As in Prob. 5, draw a curve for Prob. 1(c), showing probability against M_1.

11. In Prob. 2(b) what is the probability that, in 100 throws of the die, there will be 20 ones, 30 fours, and 50 sixes?

12. Using the equation (see Eq. 1–41)

$$P = \sqrt{\frac{2}{\pi m}}\, e^{-(2/m)\,[m_1-(m/2)]^2}$$

compute the data asked for in Prob. 7 and compare curves, remembering that the equation that is most accurate is

$$P = \frac{m!}{m_1!(m - m_1)!}\frac{1}{2^m}$$

13. (a) Using the equation (see Eq. 1–54a)

$$P = \frac{\sqrt{27}}{2\pi n} \exp\left\{-\frac{3}{4n}\left[\left(M_1 - \frac{M}{3}\right)^2 + \left(M_2 - \frac{M}{3}\right)^2\right]\right\}$$

Compute the answer to that of Eq. 8(b) and compare.

(b) Compute, using the equation in 1(a), the answer to 8(c) and compare.

(c) Can you get the equation given in Prob. 1(a) from Eq. 1–54(a) when there are just two kinds of marbles and the a priori probabilities are $\frac{1}{3}$ and $\frac{2}{3}$?

14. Two men are matching silver dollars. Mr. A has $2.00 and Mr. B has $100.00. What is the probability that at the end of exactly four throws Mr. A is exactly broke and the game has to stop? What is the probability that A has $8.00 in his pocket at the end of 4 throws and B has $92.00?

15. During a brief and light shower a small plant bearing 100 green leaves stood receiving rain at an average rate of 10 drops of rain per leaf per minute. At the end of one minute what is the probability that each leaf got 10 drops?

16. (a) If you had a bottle of 2240 cc of helium gas at 273°K at one atmosphere, do you know many atoms there would be in the bottle?

(b) If you took out a one cc sample, how many atoms do you expect would be in it?

(c) If you took out a sample that was spherical and was 200 angstroms in diameter, how many atoms would you expect it to contain? What is the probability that this sample might contain greater than 10 per cent too many atoms?

(d) If the sample mentioned in (c) had been 400 angstroms in diameter, how many atoms would you expect to be in it? What is the probability that there would be 10 per cent or more in excess of what you expect?

(e) Knowing that blue light has a wavelength of about 4000 angstroms and red light about 8000 angstroms and that the peak of Rayleigh scattering is attained by particles having a diameter of about one-twentieth of a wavelength, can you explain why the sky is blue?

17. A problem that was worked out years ago by someone of Langmuir's caliber (the reference of which is lost) is the following: A Roman soldier weighing 160 pounds whose composition was about 80 per cent water fell on the Sahara Desert in a skirmish, and being neglected in the haste of the compaign, lay on the sands and became dehydrated. The vapors of his body became diluted by the winds, and they in turn mingled with the clouds that drenched the earth and the

seas with rain. In the elapsed two thousand years let us assume that the water from the soldier's body became intimately mixed with all the water of our planet. Knowing that the earth is 4000 miles in radius and about 70 per cent covered by the oceans of average depth of the order of two miles, what number of water molecules from this man's body do you expect to be swallowed when you drink a half pint cup of tea?

18. (a) The mass of the earth is 5.975×10^{27} grams of average atomic weight 30.00. The fraction (by weight) of the earth that is gold has been estimated to be 3×10^{-9}. The atomic weight of gold is about 197 grams. If you were to pick a gram of soil (or rock) at random, what is the probability that it would be at least 90 per cent gold?

(b) If you searched the entire volume of the earth, what would be your chances, based on elementary probability, that there would be at least *one* piece weighing a gram or more that is 90 per cent gold?

(c) Would you conclude from your results in (a) and (b) that the enriched concentrations of materials such as sand and valuable ores found in the earth were accumulated by mere chance, or by numerous natural separation processes similar to those used by the chemical engineers? Name some of these processes and give examples from nature.

Table 1-10(a) THE LOGARITHMS OF FACTORIALS

n	log $n!$	n	log $n!$	n	log $n!$
1	0.000 000 0000	41	49.524 428 9249	81	120.763 212 7414
2	0.301 029 9957	42	51.147 678 2153	82	122.677 026 5938
3	0.778 151 2504	43	52.781 146 6709	83	124.596 104 6861
4	1.380 211 2417	44	54.424 599 3473	84	126.520 383 9722
5	2.079 181 2460	45	56.077 811 8611	85	128.449 802 8979
6	2.857 332 4964	46	57.740 569 6928	86	130.384 301 3492
7	3.702 430 5364	47	59.412 667 5507	87	132.323 820 6018
8	4.605 520 5234	48	61.093 908 7881	88	134.268 303 2739
9	5.559 763 0329	49	62.784 104 8681	89	136.217 693 2806
10	6.559 763 0329	50	64.483 074 8725	90	138.171 935 7900
11	7.601 155 7180	51	66.190 645 0486	91	140.130 977 1823
12	8.680 336 9641	52	67.906 648 3922	92	142.094 765 0097
13	9.794 280 3164	53	69.630 924 2618	93	144.063 247 9582
14	10.940 408 3521	54	71.363 318 0216	94	146.036 375 8118
15	12.116 499 6111	55	73.103 680 7111	95	148.014 099 4171
16	13.320 619 5938	56	74.851 868 7381	96	149.996 370 6502
17	14.551 068 5152	57	76.607 743 5938	97	151.983 142 3844
18	15.806 341 0203	58	78.371 171 5874	98	153.974 368 4601
19	17.085 094 6212	59	80.142 023 5990	99	155.970 003 6547
20	18.386 124 6169	60	81.920 174 8494	100	157.970 003 6547
21	19.708 343 9116	61	83.705 504 6844	101	159.974 325 0285
22	21.050 766 5924	62	85.497 896 3739	102	161.982 925 2003
23	22.412 494 4285	63	87.297 236 9234	103	163.995 762 4250
24	23.792 705 6702	64	89.103 416 8973	104	166.012 795 7643
25	25.190 645 6788	65	90.916 330 2540	105	168.033 985 0633
26	26.605 619 0268	66	92.735 874 1895	106	170.059 290 9286
27	28.036 982 7910	67	94.561 948 9922	107	172.088 674 7063
28	29.484 140 8223	68	96.394 457 9049	108	174.122 098 4618
29	30.946 538 8202	69	98.233 306 9957	109	176.159 524 9597
30	32.423 660 0749	70	100.078 405 0357	110	178.200 917 6449
31	33.915 021 7688	71	101.929 663 3844	111	180.246 240 6237
32	35.420 171 7471	72	103.786 995 8808	112	182.295 458 6463
33	36.938 685 6870	73	105.650 318 7410	113	184.348 537 0898
34	38.470 164 6040	74	107.519 550 4607	114	186.405 441 9411
35	40.014 232 6484	75	109.394 611 7241	115	188.466 139 7815
36	41.570 535 1491	76	111.275 425 3164	116	190.530 597 7707
37	43.138 736 8732	77	113.161 916 0415	117	192.598 783 6325
38	44.718 520 4698	78	115.054 010 6442	118	194.670 665 6398
39	46.309 585 0768	79	116.951 637 7355	119	196.746 212 6012
40	47.911 645 0682	80	118.854 727 7225	120	198.825 393 8472

Table 1-10(b)   THE LOGARITHMS OF FACTORIALS

n	$\log n!$	n	$\log n!$	n	$\log n!$
121	200.908 179 2175	161	286.880 282 1167	201	377.200 084 6975
122	202.994 539 0482	162	289.089 797 1313	202	379.505 436 0669
123	207.084 444 1597	163	291.301 984 7357	203	381.812 932 1048
124	207.177 865 8448	164	293.516 828 5837	204	384.122 562 2722
125	209.274 775 8578	165	295.734 312 5279	205	386.434 316 1333
126	211.375 146 4029	166	297.954 420 6160	206	388.748 183 3537
127	213.478 950 1239	167	300.177 137 0871	207	391.064 153 6991
128	215.586 160 0935	168	302.402 446 3688	208	393.382 217 0341
129	217.696 749 8038	169	304.630 333 0735	209	395.702 363 3202
130	219.810 693 1561	170	306.860 781 9948	210	398.024 582 6149
131	221.927 964 4518	171	309.093 778 1052	211	400.348 865 0702
132	224.048 538 3830	172	311.329 306 5521	212	402.675 200 9312
133	226.172 390 0240	173	313.567 352 6553	213	405.003 580 5346
134	228.299 494 8223	174	315.807 901 9035	214	407.333 994 3080
135	230.429 828 5908	175	318.050 939 9522	215	409.666 432 7679
136	232.563 367 4992	176	320.296 452 6200	216	412.000 886 5190
137	234.700 088 0664	177	322.544 425 8864	217	414.337 346 2529
138	236.839 967 1528	178	324.794 845 8887	218	416.675 802 7465
139	238.982 981 9530	179	327.047 698 9197	219	419.016 246 8613
140	241.129 109 9887	180	329.302 971 4248	220	421.358 669 5421
141	243.278 329 1014	181	331.560 649 9997	221	423.703 061 8158
142	245.430 617 4457	182	333.820 721 3876	222	426.049 414 7903
143	247.585 953 4832	183	336.083 172 4774	223	428.397 719 6533
144	249.744 315 9753	184	338.347 990 3004	224	430.747 967 6717
145	251.905 683 9775	185	340.615 162 0288	225	433.100 150 1898
146	254.070 036 8333	186	342.884 674 9730	226	435.454 258 6289
147	256.237 354 1681	187	345.156 516 5795	227	437.810 284 4861
148	258.407 615 8835	188	347.430 674 4288	228	440.168 219 3331
149	260.580 802 1519	189	349.707 136 2330	229	442.528 054 8154
150	262.756 893 4109	190	351.985 889 8339	230	444.889 782 6515
151	264.935 870 3582	191	354.266 923 2102	231	447.253 394 6314
152	267.117 713 9462	192	356.550 224 4299	232	449.618 882 6162
153	269.302 405 3770	193	358.835 781 7389	233	451.986 238 5373
154	271.489 926 0978	194	361.123 583 4688	234	454.355 454 3947
155	273.680 257 7960	195	363.413 618 0802	235	456.726 522 2570
156	275.873 382 3943	196	365.705 874 1515	236	459.099 434 2599
157	278.069 282 0468	197	368.000 340 3777	237	461.474 182 6059
158	280.267 939 1337	198	370.297 005 5680	238	463.850 759 5630
159	282.469 336 2580	199	372.595 858 6444	239	466.229 157 4639
160	284.673 456 2407	200	374.896 888 6400	240	468.609 368 7056

2

LIMOUSINES
AND THEATERS

Introduction

There are many everyday problems in which there are limitations restricting the operations. For example, a man might find that there are n things which he has an opportunity to do this year, each having p_j probability of success, each requiring t_j time, and each yielding π_j benefits. Under the restriction that he has only 365 days in the year, he cannot respond to all these opportunities, yet he wishes to maximize his total yield. Or a large corporation has n places to invest its money, each investment subjected to r_j risk, yielding π_j per cent interest with F funds as one limitation and A total administrative funds that are not investible as another limitation. The corporation wishes to distribute its investments I_j so as to optimize the probable profits. Young men face these kinds of problems when planning their careers; a popular debutante who wishes to get married before the age of twenty-five naturally wishes to distribute her attention between her varying qualified suitors so as to maximize her chances of a "good catch."

Chemical systems "face" the same type of problem when the system is insulated from outside influences at a given temperature and pressure with the limitations that there are just n atoms (or molecules) in the system and just E energy to be shared between them, and where the nature-driven "object" is to minimize the free energy. This chapter gives examples of such problems, involving limitations inside of which probability is free to yield the most likely results regarding distribution. Emphasis is placed on two methods of solution, and the illustrations proceed from the simplest to the practical chemical problems. We have chosen the limousine and theater problems as the simplest examples adequate to demonstrate the methods. Some chemical applications are found among the exercises at the end of this chapter.

2-1 The Limousine Problem

In order to introduce a new series of problems with added conditions, let us illustrate by using a rather artificial kind of a circumstance.

A driver has a limousine which has four sections (or long seats), and he charges three dollars for each trip from a certain hotel to the airport. The sections are numbered 0, 1, 2, 3; the zero section costs nothing, number 1 section costs \$1.00, number 2 costs \$2.00, and number 3 costs \$3.00. The artificial thing is that there are invariably just four passengers and a \$1.00 bill is the smallest change used. If any one of the passengers pays the full fare of \$3.00, the other three can go free but must sit in the zero section while he sits in section number 3. When this does happen the driver never knows beforehand which one of the four passengers is going to pay the fare, whether it will be passenger 1, 2, 3, or 4. There are just four ways by which one of the four passengers can be the one paying \$3.00. These ways are shown at the top of Table 2-1. There are just four such ways:

$$W = \frac{4!}{n_0! \, n_1! \, n_2! \, n_3!} = \frac{4!}{3! \, 0! \, 0! \, 1!} = 4$$

corresponding to the number of ways of dividing four people into four sections with three in section 0, none in sections 1 and 2, and one in section 3. If two people pay, one must pay \$2.00 and another \$1.00 and two must ride free in section 0. These ways are shown in the center of Table 2-1; the number of ways is 12 by actual count and also by the equation

$$W = \frac{4!}{n_0! \, n_1! \, n_2! \, n_3!} = \frac{4!}{2! \, 1! \, 1! \, 0!} = 12$$

Finally, if three people pay, the ways are shown at the bottom of Table 2-1; there is one passenger in section 0, three in section 1, and none paying \$2.00 or \$3.00. As before, $W = 4!/(3! \, 1! \, 0! \, 0!) = 4$ ways that the passengers can be seated. It is interesting but not of immediate importance that the total number of ways is*

*See, for example, Ref. 25, pp. 435–438.

$$W = \frac{(4 + 3 - 1)!}{(4 + 1)! \, 3!} = 20 \qquad (2\text{--}1)$$

which checks with our $4 + 12 + 4 = 20$, as computed above for the three separate cases.

Table 2-1 MONEY COLLECTED IN A FOUR-SECTION LIMOUSINE

Passenger Number		1	2	3	4	No.
Passengers Paying 1		3	0	0	0	1
		0	3	0	0	2
		0	0	3	0	3
		0	0	0	3	4
	2	2	1	0	0	1
		2	0	1	0	2
		2	0	0	1	3
		1	2	0	0	4
		1	0	2	0	5
		1	0	0	2	6
		0	2	1	0	7
		0	2	0	1	8
		0	0	2	1	9
		0	1	2	0	10
		0	1	0	2	11
		0	0	1	2	12
	3	1	1	1	0	1
		1	1	0	1	2
		1	0	1	1	3
		0	1	1	1	4

2-2 Restraining Conditions

What is important here is that there are three things that are constant: (1) the number of sections in the limousine, (2) the number of dollars spent in fare, and (3) the number of passengers. If we had also stipulated that the passengers had to be seated in such numbers that W could be a maximum, the two-passenger crowd would have been overwhelmingly favored. We could have thought of the whole thing as the problem of how one can distribute three packets of money between four boxes, with no restrictions on the number per box. This has been worked out* in general for C boxes and N distinguishable objects.

*See, for example, Ref. 25, p. 438.

$$W_T = \frac{(C + N - 1)!}{(C - 1)!\, N!} \tag{2-2}$$

We can illustrate as in Table 2-2 with six packets of money distributed between eight sections of a limousine, no change smaller than $1.00 allowed. In this table we do not show all the arrangements for a particular combination. Here 60000000 means one 6 and seven zeros in any and every order that the 6 and zeros can be arranged. There are 11 such combinations with the sum of the entries in the eight positions adding up to six.

Table 2-2 Six packets of money in eight sections

Combination Number	Combination	W		Combination Number	Combination	W
1	60000000	8		7	22200000	56
2	51000000	56		8	31110000	280
3	42000000	56		9	22110000	420
4	33000000	28		10	21111000	280
5	41100000	168		11	11111600	28
6	32100000	336		Sum		1716

The values of W in Table 2-2 are computed from*

$$W = \frac{8!}{n_1!\, n_2! \ldots n_6!} = \frac{8!}{\prod\limits_{i}^{K}(n_j!)} \tag{2-3}$$

where the kinds of packets are $K = 6$ and n_j are the number of each kind taken. If we add the W's in the columns as shown, a grand sum of 1716 is obtained, which agrees with

$$W_T = \frac{(8 + 6 - 1)!}{(8 - 1)!\, 6!} = 1716 \tag{2-4}$$

Again we have a constant amount of money (or packets of $1.00 each) and a constant number of sections, and if we had favored a high value for W we would have liked combination 9 with its 420 ways out of a total of 1726 ways. That is, one combination has almost one-fourth of the total ways in it. In fact, the four top W's add up to 76.3 per cent of the total.

Another thing we would like to demonstrate is the relative number of ways of getting $1, $2, etc. packets. To show this we do Table 2-2 over and add to it as in Table 2-3. The number of times f that a particular-sized packet occurs in a combination is

*See Eq. 1-19(c).

$$f = W_{n_j} \qquad\qquad (2\text{-}5)$$

For example, the number of times that \$1.00 occurs in combination 5 is the number of ways ($W = 168$) multiplied by size of packet ($n_1 = 2$) or 336. Along the bottom the totals are recorded. If the reader were to plot f against n_j he would see a steeply descending curve; a plot of $3(f_9 + f_6)$ for various n_j's would yield a similar curve. (The reason for multiplying by 3 is to get the scales of the graphs more nearly equal.) Thus one sees that not only do the smaller packets occur with an overwhelming greater frequency, but also that the frequency distributions for the combinations with the highest W values tend to follow the same distribution curve as that of the grand total.

Table 2-3 THE FREQUENCY f_j OF OCCURRENCE OF DIFFERENT-SIZED PACKETS

			Size of Packet						
Number	Combination	W	0	1	2	3	4	5	6
1	60000000	8	56	0	0	0	0	0	1
2	51000000	56	336	56	0	0	0	56	0
3	42000000	56	336	0	56	0	56	0	0
4	33000000	28	168	0	0	56	0	0	0
5	41100000	168	840	336	0	0	168	0	0
6	32100000	336	1680	336	336	336	0	0	0
7	22200000	56	280	0	168	0	0	0	0
8	31110000	280	224	168	0	56	0	0	0
9	22110000	420	1680	840	840	0	0	0	0
10	21111000	280	840	1120	280	0	0	0	0
11	11111100	28	56	168	0	0	0	0	0
	Totals	1726	4996	3424	1680	448	224	56	1

2-3 When the Numbers Are Larger

We do not like to overdo the recording of simple tables, all representing the same idea, but one more might help for the reader's practice. In Table 2–4 the number of packets is 8 and the sections are 12. In tabulating the combinations we have left out the zeros for brevity. We have, therefore, 8 kinds of packets. The table indicates the possible values of n_j and the values of W. These numbers are usable for applying Eq. 2–5 in order to compute the frequencies of a particular packet, as recorded in Table 2–3. These computations as well as the graphs are left to the reader. Before passing it is well to notice that

Table 2-4 THE POSSIBLE n_j's IN EIGHT PACKETS AND TWELVE SECTIONS

				Designator j						
Combination	8	7	6	5	4	3	2	1	0	W
8	1								11	12
71		1						1	10	132
62			1				1		10	132
611			1					2	9	
53				1		1			10	132
521				1			1	1	9	1,320
5111				1				3	8	1,980
44					2				10	66
432					1	1	1		9	1,320
422					1		1		9	660
4211					1		1	2	8	5,940
41111					1			4	7	3,960
3221						1	2	1	8	5,940
32111						1	1	3	7	15,840
311111						1		5	6	27,720
2222							4		8	495
22211							3	2	7	7,920
221111							2	4	6	20,790
2111111							1	6	5	5,544
11111111								8	4	495
								Total		75,582

the sum of the three top W's is 85 per cent of the grand total.

If we were to continue making tables like these with increasing numbers of packets n and increasing sections or kinds of packets K, we would find an increasing tendency for one of the W's to dominate the column of W's so that $W_{\max}$ would approach W_T as n and K approach infinity and the ln $W_{\max}$ would differ from ln W_T by negligible amounts. The general problem before us is to fulfill three conditions in getting the most probable distribution of passengers in a limousine (theater, ocean liner, etc.). The conditions are

$$\sum_{j=1}^{K} n_j = n \tag{2–6a}$$

$$\sum_{j=1}^{j=K} e_j n_j = E \tag{2–6b}$$

$$W(n_1 n_2 \cdots n_K) = W_{\max} \tag{2–6c}$$

where e_j is the price of a seat in a section and n_j is the number in each section. In the above example all the e_j's were the same and consequently do not represent the general case. Such a charging system is called here a "flat-rate" enterprise.

The ultimate object of introducing these examples is to make the reader feel secure in his methods of computing distributions of people in sections (or quanta on atoms). We first have to give a more general example and then describe the two methods of computation: (1) the method of undetermined multipliers and (2) a method which is furnished by Gurney.*

2-4 The Linear-Rate Theater (Harmonic Plaza)

Let us suppose that in a certain town there is just one theater. At the ticket window the smallest coin of change that is used is e (say 25 cents) and all prices are some multiple of this. The manager knows this community fairly well and has observed that there are exactly n people attending each weekly performance. He also has observed that the economic status of the community provides just E units of cash to be spent on entertainment each week. The theater is divided into K sections and there is one dingy section that is free so that $e_0 = 0e = 0$; the first section is priced at e, the second at $2e$, the third at $3e$, etc. The money taken in is

$$E = \sum_{j=0}^{K} e_j n_j = e \sum_{j=0}^{K} jn_j \qquad (2\text{-}7a)$$

It is because of the fact that $e_j = je$ that we call this a linear-rate theater. The total number of people is

$$n = \sum_{j=0}^{K} n_j \qquad (2\text{-}7b)$$

The number of ways of distributing the people between these K sections is

$$W = \frac{n!}{\prod_{0}^{K}(n_j!)} \qquad (2\text{-}7c)$$

We shall notice that the expression for W in Eq. 2-7(c) does not contain e_j, and is not a function of e_j. But Eq. 2-7(a) is a condition involving e_j which must be fulfilled, and any value of W that does not comply must be discarded. So there are three equations 2-7(a-c) which must be satisfied simultaneously in order to solve for the optimum distribution n_j of people throughout the K sections of the

*Reference 16, pp. 13–26.

theater. There are two methods which are to be discussed here for solving these equations: (1) the method of undetermined multipliers and (2) the method which is furnished by Gurney. We will digress for a moment to describe these methods and then return to Eqs. 2–7(a–c).

2-5 The Method of Undetermined Multipliers*

Sometimes one wishes to find the conditions for making a function a maximum or a minimum when the variables inside the function are connected by known relations. For this purpose Lagrange devised the method of undetermined multipliers. Although simple problems can be solved by more direct methods, more complicated problems are easier to handle by Lagrange's methods. Although many texts explain and derive the equations involved, we plan here to induce familiarity by supplying a number of illustrations. The only thing we have to say that has any theatrical significance is that any curve which has a maximum or minimum at a point has zero slope at that point, and therefore its derivative is zero at that point.

A. We have a wire whose length is W, and we wish to make a rectangle from this wire having maximum area A of length L and width D to be determined. In this problem W is the thing that is fixed, A is the thing to be maximized, and they are both related through L and D.

$$A = A(LD) = LD \tag{2–8a}$$

$$W = W(LD) = 2L + 2D \tag{2–8b}$$

Differentiating these equations and setting to zero, we have

$$dA = L\,dD + D\,dL = 0 \tag{2–9a}$$

$$dW = 2\,dD + 2\,dL = 0 \tag{2–9b}$$

Multiplying 2–9(b) by λ and adding to 2–9(a) gives

$$(L + 2\lambda)\,dD + (D + 2\lambda)\,dL = 0$$

which is true if $L = D$, and therefore the wire is to be formed into a square.

B. An example from Myron Tribus† gives a good chance to illustrate the use of more than one value of λ. It has to do with the manufacture of tin cans having diameter D and height L. The thing

*For a discussion of this method, see Ref. 35, p. 69, and also I. S. and E. S. Sokolnikoff, *Higher Mathematics for Engineers and Physicists* (New York: McGraw-Hill, 1934, p. 127.

†Reference 35, p. 72.

to be minimized is the cost ϕ of the can. This cost includes the cost of the metal, which in turn is proportioned to the area A of the can (since the can is uniform in thickness and the cost of metal per pound is fixed). The cost of the can also includes the cost of welding the seams, which is proportional to the length W of the seams. The seams go around the top and bottom of the can, and there is one seam up the side. Let C_m be the cost per unit area of the metal and C_w be the cost per unit length of the weld. We want the volume V of the can to be high and the cost ϕ to be low. The initial equations of condition are

$$\phi = C_m A + C_w W \tag{2-10a}$$

$$A = \pi DL + \frac{2\pi D^2}{4} \tag{2-10b}$$

$$W = 2\pi D + L \tag{2-10c}$$

$$V = \frac{\pi D^2}{4} L \tag{2-10d}$$

Differentiating each of these equations, multiplying the second by λ_1, the third by λ_2, and the last by λ_3, and equating to zero gives

$$d\phi - (C_m \, dA + C_w \, dW) = 0 \tag{2-11a}$$

$$\lambda_1 \, dA - (\lambda_1 \pi D \, dL + \lambda_1 \pi L \, dD + \lambda_1 \pi D \, dD) = 0 \tag{2-11b}$$

$$\lambda_2 \, dW - (\lambda_2 2\pi \, dD + \lambda_2 dL) = 0 \tag{2-11c}$$

$$\lambda_3 \, dV - \left(\lambda_3 \frac{\pi D^2 \, dL}{4} + \lambda_3 \frac{2\pi DL \, dD}{4}\right) = 0 \tag{2-11d}$$

Adding these equations, we find (since $d\phi = 0$)

$$(\lambda_1 - C_m) \, dA + (\lambda_2 - C_w) \, dW = 0$$

$$-\left(\lambda_1 \pi L + \lambda_1 \pi D + \lambda_2 2\pi + \lambda_3 \frac{2\pi DL}{4}\right) dD = 0 \tag{2-12}$$

$$-\left(\lambda_1 \pi D + \lambda_2 + \frac{\lambda_3 \pi D^2}{4}\right) dL = 0$$

Equating each part to zero, we get

$$\lambda_1 = C_m$$

$$\lambda_2 = C_w$$

$$\lambda_3 = \frac{2(L + D)}{LD} C_m - \frac{4C_w}{DL}$$

and substituting these values into the dD part of Eq. 2-12 gives

$$C_m \pi D + C_w - \frac{\pi DC_m(L + D)}{2L} - \frac{\pi DC_w}{L} = 0$$

This is an equation in two unknowns, D and L. One of these can be eliminated through Eq. 2-10(d), since V is fixed, and we can get an equation in one unknown:

$$\pi C_m D^4 + 2\pi C_w D^3 - 4V C_m D - \frac{8V C_w}{\pi} = 0$$

which must be solved graphically.

2-6 Lagrange's Method Applied to the Linear-Rate Theater

Before we apply Lagrange's method to Eq. 2-7(a-c), let us state that when a variable reaches its maximum value so does its logarithm. In 2-7(c) the $\ln W$ is (Stirling's approximation being used)

$$\ln W = n \ln n - \Sigma n_j \ln n_j$$

Differentiating this by parts, we have

$$d \ln W = -\Sigma \left(n_j \frac{dn_j}{n_j} + \ln n_j \, dn_j \right) = -\Sigma (1 + \ln n_j) \, dn_j$$

Neglecting the 1 compared to $\ln n_j$, we have, after differentiating and equating 2-7(a) and 2-7(b) to zero, three equations:

$$\Sigma e_j \, dn_j = 0 \qquad (2\text{-}13a)$$

$$\Sigma dn_j = 0 \qquad (2\text{-}13b)$$

$$\Sigma \ln n_j \, dn_j = 0 \qquad (2\text{-}13c)$$

Now, multiplying the first of these by μ and the second by λ and adding gives a single equation:

$$\Sigma (\ln n_j + \lambda + \mu e_j) \, dn_j = 0$$

or

$$\ln n_j + \lambda + \mu e_j = 0 \qquad \text{(term by term for reasonable values of } j\text{)}$$

or

$$n_j = e^{-(\lambda + \mu e_j)} = e^{-\lambda} e^{-\mu e_j} \qquad (2\text{-}14)$$

As before in the use of undetermined multipliers, we have to solve for them. Substituting Eq. 2-14 into 2-7(b) gives

$$n = \sum_{j=0}^{K} n_j = \sum_{j=0}^{K} e^{-(\lambda + \mu e_j)} = e^{-\lambda} \Sigma e^{-\mu e_j} \qquad (2\text{-}14a)$$

Let us designate the summation as the "partition function," Q (which will take on more significance later)

$$n = e^{-\lambda}Q$$

or

$$e^{-\lambda} = \frac{n}{Q} \qquad (2\text{--}15)$$

Combining Eqs. 2–14 and 2–15 yields

$$n_j = \frac{ne^{-\mu e_j}}{Q}$$

or if

$$e_j = je,$$

$$n_j = \frac{e^{-\mu je}n}{Q} \qquad (2\text{--}16)$$

Equation 2–16 shows that a plot of n_j against j should give a rapidly descending curve, as was indicated regarding graphs for Tables 2–3 and 2–4.

It is of interest for future thinking to substitute Eq. 2–16 into Eq. 2–7(a)

$$E = \sum_{0}^{K} e_j n_j = \sum je\,\frac{N}{Q}\,e^{-\mu je}$$

$$= \frac{ne}{Q}\,\sum je^{-\mu e_j}$$

$$= \frac{ne}{Q}\,(0 + e^{-\mu e} + 2e^{-2\mu e} + 3e^{-3\mu e}\ldots) \qquad (2\text{--}17)$$

$$= \frac{ne}{Q}\,e^{-\mu e}(1 + 2e^{-\mu e} + 3e^{-2\mu e} + 4e^{-3\mu e}\ldots)$$

If we think of $e^{-\mu e}$ as x in this equation, it resembles Eq. 826 of Peirce's tables, p. 98; for a linear-rate theater the total gate receipts are

$$E = \frac{ne}{Q}\,\frac{e^{-\mu e}}{(1 - e^{-\mu e})^2} \qquad (2\text{--}18)$$

We will postpone the actual evaluation of μ until later.

2-7 The Method from Gurney* Applied to the Linear-Rate Theater

We are now going to illustrate a very clever method presented by Gurney for maximizing W as in Eq. 2–7(c). We know from Sec. 1–15 and Figs. 1–3 and 1–4 that equations like 2–7(c) give a K-dimensional

*Reference 16, pp. 21–26.

Gaussian "curve" and at the point of maximum W in the $(n_1, n_2 \ldots n_j \ldots n_K)$ domain, the slope with respect to all $(n_j - n_j^*)$ is zero (where n_j^* is the n_j for maximum W). We also know that the hill is somewhat "flattish" on top, so that the n_j values could be varied somewhat without changing W very much. We can use this invariance of W with small changes in n_j near $W_{\max}$ as a criterion for optimum distribution. Let $W_{\max}$ be expressed as follows:

$$W_{\max} = \frac{n!}{n_1^*! \, n_2^*! \, n_3^*! \ldots n_K^*!}$$

$$= \frac{n!}{n_1^*! \ldots n_h^*! \ldots n_j^*! \ldots n_m^*! \ldots n_K^*!} \qquad (2\text{-}19)$$

Without changing the total number n, we will take $(p + q)$ people out of the jth section of the theater and leave $(n_j - p - q)$ people in it. Then place p of these people in section h and q of the people in section m so that section h now has $(n_h + p)$ people in it and section m has $(n_m + q)$ people. The number of ways of arranging the people is now

$$W = \frac{n!}{n_1^*! \ldots (n_h^* + p)! \ldots (n_j - p - q)! \ldots (n_m^* + q)!} \qquad (2\text{-}20)$$

If the value of W has not been altered much in this change of people in sections, then the ratio of $W/W_{\max} = 1$.

Since the unaltered n_j's cancel, we get

$$1 = \frac{W}{W_{\max}} = \frac{n_K^*! \, n_j^*! \, n_m^*!}{(n_h^* + p)! \, (n_j^* - p - q)! \, (n_m^* + q)!}$$

$$\doteq \frac{(n_j^*)^{(p+q)}}{(n_h^*)^p (n_m^*)^q} \qquad (2\text{-}21)$$

At the same time that we are conserving people (i.e., maintaining constant n), we have to maintain constant gate receipts E. In this linear-rate theater the following balance of money applies:

$$pe_h + qe_m = (p + q)e_j \qquad (2\text{-}22)$$

which expresses the thought that sections h and m gain the same money that section j loses.

From Eq. 2-22 we can solve for p.

$$p = q\left(\frac{e_m - e_j}{e_j - e_h}\right)$$

Substituting Eq. 2-22 into 2-21, we have

$$n_h^{q(e_m - e_j / e_j - e_h)} n_m^q = n_j^{q[1 + (e_m - e_j / e_j - e_h)]}$$

Take the qth root of both sides.

$$n_h^{(e_m-e_j/e_j-e_h)} n_m = n_j n_j^{(e_m-e_j/e_j-e_h)}$$

or (2-23)

$$n_m = n_j \left(\frac{n_j}{n_h}\right)^{(e_m-e_j/e_j-e_h)}$$

Equation 2-23 does not depend upon whether the theater uses a flat rate, a linear rate, or any other system of charges. It also does not depend upon the choice of the values of m, j, or h. If we let $h=0$ and $j=1$,

$$n_m = n_1 \left(\frac{n_1}{n_0}\right)^{(e_m-e_1/e_1-e_0)}$$ (2-24)

We will use Eq. 2-24 as a reference equation for the various kinds of theaters.

In the case of the linear-rate theater we had $e_j = je$, where e was the unit of smallest change. So in Eq. 2-24 we have $e_m = me$, $e_1 = e$ and $e_0 = 0$. This gives us

$$n_m = n_1 \left(\frac{n_1}{n_0}\right)^{m-1}$$

or

$$n_m = \frac{n_0}{n_1} \left(\frac{n_1}{n_0}\right)^m = n_0 \left(\frac{n_0}{n_1}\right)^{-m}$$ (2-25)

We can reinsert e_m in this equation.

$$n_m = n_0 \left(\frac{n_0}{n_1}\right)^{-e_m/m}$$

$$= n_0 e^{[-(e_m/m) \ln \ln (n_0/n_1)]} = e^{-\ln(1/n_0)} e^{-[\ln(n_0/n_1)](e_m/m)}$$ (2-26)

This equation looks to be much of the form of Eq. 2-14 where

$$\mu = \frac{\ln n_1}{m \ n_0} \quad \text{and} \quad \lambda = \ln \frac{1}{n_0}$$

2-8 More about A Priori Probability

At this time it is well that we fulfill a promise that we made in a previous section, that is, that we would show circumstances under which the a priori probability differs from $1/K$ for reasons other than that of having a different number of boxes in each group as in the shower of sand. In the present examples using theaters the flat-rate theater *could* have varying numbers of seats in each section, causing

$$p_j = \frac{v_j}{K}$$

although this would be artificial. But the placing of a different price on each of the jth sections ($e_j = je$) also has an effect on the a priori probability regardless of the number ν_j seats in the jth section as long as ν_j is large enough to accommodate the people. An equation that is always reliable for computing a priori probability is

$$p_j = \frac{n_j^*}{n} \tag{2-27}$$

where n_j^* is the most probable number of people in the jth section. Accepting Eq. 2-14 as an expression of n_j, we have

$$p_j = \frac{e^{-\lambda}e^{-\mu e_j}}{n} = \frac{e^{-\lambda}e^{-\mu e_j}}{\sum n_j} = \frac{e^{-\lambda}e^{-\mu e_j}}{\sum e^{-\lambda}e^{-\mu e_j}}$$

$$= \frac{e^{-\mu e_j}}{\sum e^{-\mu e_j}} = \frac{e^{-\mu e_j}}{Q} \tag{2-28}$$

Or using Eq. 2-26, we have

$$p_j = \frac{e^{-\ln(n_0/n_1)e_j}}{Q} \tag{2-29}$$

For the flat-rate theater $e_j = e$ for all j, so

$$p_j = \frac{e^{-\mu e}}{\sum e^{-\mu e_j}} = \frac{e^{-\mu e}}{Ke^{-\mu e}} = \frac{1}{K} \tag{2-30}$$

as expected, but for the linear-rate theater ($e_j = je$)

$$p_j = \frac{e^{-\mu je}}{\sum e^{-\mu je}} = \frac{x^j}{\sum x^j} = \frac{x^j}{1 + x + x^2 \dots}$$

where $x = e^{-\mu e}$ (see Peirce's tables, p. 98, Eq. 823).

$$p_j = x^j(1 - x) = e^{-\mu je}(1 - e^{-\mu e}) \tag{2-31}$$

(if K is great).

2-9 The Squared-Rate Theater

As an example of a squared rate, we have a theater divided into six sections numbered 0, 1, 2, 3, 4, and 5. These are the j numbers. The prices of these sections are $e_j = j^2 e$, where e is the smallest bit of change allowed. Therefore, the prices are $0, e, 4e, 9e, 16e$, and $25e$. These prices (neglecting the symbol e) are tabulated across the third set of columns in Table 2-5. We also stipulate that the total receipts amount to $E = 25e$ from the number of people, $n = 30$; so that if one person sits in the $25e$ priced section, all the remaining 29 people must sit in the zero-priced section. In Table 2-5, 1(25) means one person sitting in a $25e$ section and the rest in zero, and 2(9) 1(4) 4(1)

Table 2-5

| | No. of Each Kind | | | | | | | | Frequency | | | | | |
Kinds	25	16	9	4	1	0	ln W	W	25	16	9	4	1	0
1. 1(25)	1					29	1.40	2.5×10^1	1	0	0	0	0	7.25×10^1
2. 1(16) 1(9)		1	1			28	2.94	8.7×10^2	0	8.6×10^2	8.7×10^2	0	0	2.33×10^4
3. 1(16) 2(4) 1(1)		1		2	1	26	5.92	8.3×10^5	0	8.8×10^5	0	1.75×10^6	8.26×10^5	2.14×10^7
4. 1(16) 1(4) 4(1)		1		1	5	23	7.93	8.5×10^7	0	8.6×10^7	0	8.55×10^7	3.4×10^8	1.96×10^9
5. 1(16) 9(1)		1			9	20	8.48	3.0×10^8	0	3.0×10^8	0	0	2.7×10^9	1.695×10^{10}
6. 2(9) 1(4) 4(1)			2	1	3	24	7.55	3.60×10^7	0	0	7.1×10^7	3.55×10^7	1.1×10^8	8.52×10^8
7. 2(9) 7(1)			2		7	21	8.71	5.1×10^8	0	0	1.1×10^9	0	3.6×10^9	1.28×10^{10}
8. 1(9) 4(4)			1	4		25	5.85	7.1×10^5	0	0	7.1×10^5	X	0	X
9. 1(9) 3(4) 4(1)			1	3	4	22	9.22	1.6×10^9	0	0	1.6×10^9	X	X	X
10. 1(9) 2(4) 8(1)			1	2	8	19	10.43	2.7×10^{10}	0	0	2.7×10^{10}	5.4×10^{10}	X	X
11. 1(9) 1(4) 12(1)			1	1	12	16	10.42	2.7×10^{10}	0	0	2.6×10^{10}	2.65×10^{10}	X	X
12. 1(9) 16(1)			1		16	13	9.31	2.09×10^9	0	0	2.04×10^9	0	X	X
13. 6(4) 1(1)				6	1	23	7.15	1.4×10^7	0	0	0	X	1.42×10^7	X
14. 5(4) 5(1)				5	5	20	9.88	7.6×10^9	0	0	0	X	X	X
15. 4(4) 9(1)				4	9	17	10.93	8.69×10^{10}	0	0	0	3.42×10^{11}	7.7×10^{11}	1.45×10^{12}
16. 3(4) 13(1)				3	13	14	10.91	8.1×10^{10}	0	0	0	X	X	X
17. 2(4) 17(1)				2	17	11	9.97	9.4×10^9	0	0	0	X	X	X
18. 1(4) 21(1)				1	21	8	8.11	1.3×10^8	0	0	0	1.29×10^8	X	X
19. 25(1)					25	5	5.15	1.4×10^5	0	0	0	X	X	X

The spaces marked X have not been computed.

53

means 2 people in $9e$ section, 1 person in $4e$, and 4 people in e. One can see again in this table the tendency for certain combinations to be extremely fruitful in ways W.

Using the Gurney method, we find that Eq. 2–24 still holds, but the values of e_m, e_1, and e_0 are m^2e, e, and 0 respectively, so

$$n_j = n_1 \left(\frac{n_1}{n_0}\right)^{(j^2e-e)/(e-0)} = n_1 \left(\frac{n_1}{n_0}\right)^{j^2-1}$$

$$\doteq n_0 \left(\frac{n_0}{n_1}\right)^{-j^2} \tag{2-32}$$

or in general

$$n_j = n_0 \left(\frac{n_0}{n_1}\right)^{-(e_j/e)} = n_0 e^{-(e_j/e)\ln(n_0/n_1)} \tag{2-33}$$

We will use Eq. 2–22 to show the procedure for finding the values of n_0 and n_1 knowing n, the number of people, and E, the total cash taken in.

$$n = \Sigma\, n_j = \Sigma\, n_0 \left(\frac{n_0}{n_1}\right)^{-j^2} = n_0 \int_0^K e^{-j^2\ln(n_0/n_1)} \tag{2-34}$$

Here we have replaced m by j in Eq. 2–26.

Equation 2–34 is of the form

$$y = \int_0^\infty e^{-a^2x^2}\,dx$$

which has (according to Peirce's table, p. 68, Eq. 507) the solution

$$y = \frac{\sqrt{\pi}}{2a}$$

So

$$n = \frac{n_0\sqrt{\pi}}{2\sqrt{\ln(n_0/n_1)}} \tag{2-35}$$

Solving for n_1 from Eq. 2–35 gives for the number of people in the first section

$$n_1 = n_0 e^{-(\pi/4)(n_0/n)^2}$$

Putting this value of n_1 into Eq. 2–33 gives

$$n_j = n_0 e^{-(\pi/4)(n_0/n)^2(e_j/e)} = n_0 e^{-(\pi/4)(n_0/n)^2 j^2} \tag{2-36}$$

We can solve for n_0 by knowing that

$$E = \sum_0^K n_j e_j = \Sigma\, j^2 \exp^{-(\pi/4)(n_0/n)^2 j^2} \doteq e \int j^2 e^{-(\pi/4)(n_0/n)^2 j^2}\, dj$$

This equation is of the form

$$y = \int_0^\infty x^2 e^{-ax^2} dx = \frac{1}{2^2 a}\sqrt{\frac{\pi}{a}}$$

(according to Peirce's tables, p. 63, Eq. 494). So

$$E = \frac{2en^3}{\pi n_0^2}$$

$$n_0 = \left(\frac{2en^3}{\pi E}\right)^{1/2}$$

(2-37)

When this is introduced into Eq. 2-36, then

$$n_j = \left(\frac{2en}{\pi E}\right)^{1/2} ne^{-(ne/2E)j^2}$$

(2-38)

Or, introducing the concept of average price per person $\bar{e} = E/n$, we have

$$n_j = \left(\frac{2e}{\bar{e}}\right)^{1/2} ne^{-(ej^2/2\bar{e})}$$

(2-39)

2-10 The Partition Function

At this time we can get more practice on the concept of the partition function by solving for the a priori probability p_j.

$$p_j = \frac{n_j}{n} = \frac{n_j}{\Sigma\, n_j} = \frac{\left(\dfrac{2e}{\bar{e}}\right)^{1/2} ne^{-(ej^2/2\bar{e})}}{\left(\dfrac{2e}{\bar{e}}\right)^{1/2} n\, \Sigma\, e^{-(ej^2/2\bar{e})}}$$

$$= \frac{e^{-ej^2/2\bar{e}}}{\Sigma\, e^{-ej^2/2\bar{e}}} = \frac{e^{-ej^2/2\bar{e}}}{Q}$$

(2-40)

The type of equation shown is easily put in general form by replacing e_j^2 by e_j to get an equation that *always* applies regardless of the price scale (that is, for all types of theaters or limousines),

$$p_j = \frac{e^{-e_j/2\bar{e}}}{Q}$$

(2-41)

and

$$Q = \sum_{j=1}^{K} e^{-e_j/2\bar{e}}$$

(2-42)

In fact, Eqs. 2-41 and 2-42 will even apply to atoms and molecules (see Problems).

2-11   Summary

Let us write some general equations and then apply them to the three kinds of theaters. The general equations:

$$Q = \sum_{j=1}^{K} e^{-e_j/2\bar{e}} \tag{2-43a}$$

where e_j is some function of j as before.

$$p_j = \frac{e^{-e_j/2\bar{e}}}{Q} \tag{2-43b}$$

$$n_j = np_j = \frac{ne^{-e_j/2\bar{e}}}{Q} \tag{2-43c}$$

$$\ln W = -np_j \ln p_j \tag{2-43d}$$

Using Eqs. 2–43(a–d), we get the equations for the flat-rate theater:

$$Q = \sum_{0}^{K} e^{-e_j/2\bar{e}} = Ke^{-1/2} \tag{2-44a}$$

where $e_j = \bar{e}$ for all j's.

$$p_j = \frac{1}{K} \tag{2-44b}$$

$$n_j = \frac{n}{K} \tag{2-44c}$$

$$\ln W = n \ln K \tag{2-44d}$$

The equations for the linear-rate theater are

$$Q = \sum_{j=0}^{K} e^{-je/2\bar{e}} = \frac{e^{-e/2\bar{e}}}{1 - e^{-e/2\bar{e}}} \tag{2-45a}$$

$$p_j = \frac{e^{-je/2\bar{e}}}{Q} \tag{2-45b}$$

$$n_j = \frac{ne^{-je/2\bar{e}}}{Q} \tag{2-45c}$$

$$\ln W = \frac{E}{2\bar{e}} + \ln Q \tag{2-45d}$$

The equations for the squared-rate theater are

$$Q = \sum_{j} e^{-j^2e/2\bar{e}} \tag{2-46a}$$

$$p_j = \frac{e^{-j^2e/2\bar{e}}}{Q} \tag{2-46b}$$

$$n_j = \frac{ne^{-ej^2/2\bar{e}}}{Q} \tag{2-46c}$$

$$\ln W = -n \sum p_j \ln p_j$$

$$= -n \sum \frac{e^{-ej^2/2\bar{e}}}{Q} \ln \frac{e^{-ej^2/2\bar{e}}}{Q}$$

$$= \frac{n}{Q} \sum e^{-ej^2/2\bar{e}} \left(\frac{ej^2}{2\bar{e}} + \ln Q\right)$$

$$= \frac{n}{2\bar{e}Q} \sum ej^2 e^{-ej^2/2\bar{e}} + \frac{n \ln Q}{Q} \sum e^{-ej^2/2\bar{e}}$$

$$= \frac{E}{2\bar{e}} + \ln Q \tag{2-46d}$$

Equation 2-46(d) is the same as Eq. 2-45(d) and in this form is universal. We shall use it multiplied by $2\bar{e}$.

$$2\bar{e} \ln W = E + 2\bar{e} \ln Q \tag{2-47}$$

or

$$-2\bar{e} \ln Q = E - 2\bar{e} \ln W \tag{2-47a}$$

because of its relation to the equation in chemistry

$$F = E - TS$$

where F is Helmholtz's free energy.

PROBLEMS

1. (a) Using Table 2–3, make a histogram, plotting in the y direction the *totals* (as tabulated along the base of the table) against size of packet 1, 2, 3, 4, 5, and 6 in the x direction. Pass a smooth curve through points. Note the steep descent of the curve.

(b) Make a similar histogram, plotting the numbers in row 5 of the table against size of packet. (*Hint*: to keep this plot on the same scale as the one in 1(a), one can multiply the numbers by three. Do the same with the numbers in row 10.)

(c) Using a scale factor of two, make a plot of row 9.

(d) Without using a scale factor, add the numbers in rows 5, 10, and 9 and make a plot against the size of packet. After drawing a smooth curve, compare this result with that obtained in 1(a).

2. Use the method of undetermined multipliers to solve the following problems:

(a) A pioneer farmer wants to go to the trading post over rough mountain roads in a wagon and team that is capable of hauling only 1000 lb of produce to feed his cow. He thinks that carbohydrates are the only ingredient of food worth considering, and he has been told (rightly or wrongly) that the richest thing he can buy is concentrated sorghum molasses, which is 85 per cent carbohydrates; next is corn, 50 per cent; ordinary hay is about 25 per cent digestible carbohydrates. He is told correctly that the molasses is 3 cents a pint, corn is 50 cents per hundred pounds, and hay 12 cents per 50 lb bale. With $5.00 in his pocket, what are the quantities of molasses, corn, and hay that he will buy to get the greatest quantity of carbohydrates home?

(b) An investment firm has one million dollars to invest in four companies A, B, C, and D. Company A requires a litigation cost (including a number of items such as conferences, lawyers, sales visitors, etc.) of only 1 per cent and pays 6 per cent interest; B costs 4 per cent and pays 11 per cent; C costs 3 per cent and pays 7 per cent; D costs nothing and pays 5 per cent. While the entire one million dollars is used to buy the stocks in the four companies, the boards of directors have allowed twenty thousand dollars to pay litigation fees. How should the investments be distributed among the companies to get the greatest return in interest on the investment the first year?

(c) The Students' Welfare League has collected all the questions that Professor Arthur Arsnik has asked in freshman chemistry for the last 31 years. There are 201 questions in all, numbered $1, 2, 3, \ldots, j, \ldots,$ 201, and their frequencies of being asked are tabulated as v; the time required to memorize the correct answer is t_j. The value of each question is v_j. There are n hours of study time between the last meeting of the glee club and the examination bell. There are 10 questions to be asked (a passing grade is 60) and n is a small number compared to the time to learn chemistry. How should the cramming time be distributed between the questions? (Beware of extraneous data.)

    3. A child has a sand bucket full of marbles which he throws up a long flight of stairs. The number of marbles is n and the energy that the child can deliver to the throw is E. The stair steps are numbered $1, 2, \ldots, j, \ldots, n$ and the gravitational energy difference between steps per marble is ϵ. Compute the most probable distribution n_j of marbles landing on each of the thickly carpeted stair steps.

    4. Using the Gurney method, derive the distribution equations applicable to a squared-rate theater.

    5. Using Lagrange's method, solve Prob. 4.

6. If the child in Prob. 3 were to drop the marbles from on high on a flat checkered carpet of m equal-sized squares, how would the problem correspond to a flat-rate theater?

7. If a glass tube about two inches in diameter and 400 miles long, with a stopper in the bottom, were stood on end, had nitrogen gas pumped into it until the pressure on the bottom was one atmosphere, and if it were heated at a uniform temperature $T = 293°K$ so that gravimetric energy would be the only energy that is a function of height, what would be the concentration of gas in atoms per cc at various heights h? Assume that the tube is perfectly insulated and the energy of the system is E. (*Note:* there are several ways to approach the problem. One method is given in Ref. 26, p. 67.)

8. Suppose there were two liquids which would not mix in a graduated column. One of them is denser than the other, so that liquid A floats on liquid B. A and B occupy equal volumes. A third substance C is soluble in both; a small amount of this has been added, and time for equilibrium has been allowed. The average energy per molecule is $\bar{e}$ if you wish to use it, and the total energy is E. The heat of solution of C in A is ΔE_A and of C in B is ΔE_B. What are the relative concentrations of C in A and B?

9. (a) Given an alloy $M_x N_y$, where the metal M is at one kind of sites (1) and metal N is at the (2) sites. Of course, the proportion of (1) and (2) sites is as x to y according to the formula $M_x N_y$. Suppose some gas atoms were permitted to adsorb on the surface of a piece of this metal, but not in great enough quantity to cover all the sites. What would be the relative abundance of gas atoms on the two kinds of sites?

(b) If the energies of adsorption had the ratio $\Delta E_{(1)}/\Delta E_{(2)} = R$, what would be the relative ratio of occupied (1) and (2) sites?

ATOMS
AND MOLECULES

Introduction

In Chapter 2 we spent much time in discussing people in limousines and theaters in preparation for discussions of atoms and molecules. This was not made possible because people and atoms have very much in common nor because theaters are like beakers, but only because of one resemblance for each of these things. Theaters, like beakers, have a limited capacity; people and molecules each have a limitation: people have limited money, and atoms or molecules in an insulated container have a limited energy to share between them. To make the analogies more complete we had to impose an artificial characteristic on money, namely that money as paid as fare or for theater tickets is transferred only in multiples of a discrete packet, such as one dollar or some quantity equal to the price of the first section. In dealing with energy in molecules this is not artificial. Quantum mechanics tells us how big this packet of energy is for each kind of a system. This chapter correlates the problems of theaters with problems in chemistry.

3-1 Some Correlations

The concepts of probability that we have applied to the study of our special kinds of theaters applies also to large aggregates of molecules and atoms. The reader will notice the analogy between n atoms (or molecules) in a given space with a total constant energy E shared between them and a theater containing n people who have paid E in gate receipts to get in. One can correlate the smallest divisible part of the energy shared among the atoms as a number e to be determined from quantum mechanics. The amount of energy assigned to any atom is a packet of these energy units called e_j. The energy in the packet is $e_j = ef(j)$, where $f(j)$ means "some function of j." As in the prices of tickets to various sections of the theatre, these packets might contain $e_j = e, e_j = ej, e_j = ej^2$ or any other scale that is necessary. There are many ways of distributing the packets of energy among the atoms, just as there were many ways of distributing money among people. But we reverse the problem from the distribution of energy between atoms to that of distributing atoms among energy classes, or "energy levels," as they are called. This switch is demonstrated in the theater problems in Tables 2–2, 2–3, and 2–4, where it was noticed that when large numbers n and k are considered, the distribution on the grand scale fits closely that combination of divisions of people (atoms) which can happen in the largest number of ways.

Just as with people in the theater, we can assume that the atoms can be classified according to their energy state. The states are numbered $0, 1, 2, \ldots, j, \ldots, K$ just as were the sections of the theater. The distribution of atoms between the energy levels is analogous to the distribution of people among the sections of the theater. The set of equations 2–43(a–d) apply without alteration to the general problems involving aggregates of atoms or molecules. For example, 2–43(c) gives the distribution of atoms in the energy levels, that is, the number n_j of atoms having energy e_j,

$$n_j = \frac{ne^{-e_j/2\bar{e}}}{Q} = \frac{ne^{-[ef(j)/2\bar{e}]}}{Q} \tag{3-1}$$

where three things are to be furnished; we need to know (1) $\bar{e}$, the average energy per atom, (2) e, the size of the smallest packet of energy, and (3) $f(j)$, the function of j. We must digress a moment before attempting to assign values to the first and last of these, namely, $\bar{e}$ and $f(j)$.

3-2 Information Theory*

The first development of information theory by Shannon† is considered a wonderful step forward in the theory of communications. It has been

*In Ref. 5, Brillouin has given an interesting, clear, and broad view of information theory.

†C. E. Shannon and W. Weaver, *The Mathematical Theory of Communication* (Urbana, Illinois: University of Illinois Press, 1949). Also C. E. Shannon, "Prediction and Entropy of Printed English," *Bell System Tech. Journal*, **30** (1951), 50–64.

treated by many authors since, and some authors have extended the basic concepts to fields other than the sending of messages. We will give here only those aspects of information theory that are most essential for our purposes.

The first application of the theory pertained to the sending of dot and dash symbols over a wire, i.e., using the Morse code. The first question is how many distinctly different messages can be produced from combinations of n_1 dots and dashes. This is no different a number than the number of ways one expects from n_1 throws of a two-sided coin. Equation 1-5 tells us that this is

$$W_1 = 2^{n_1} \tag{3-2}$$

But the trouble with using Eq. 1-5 is that 2^{n_1} turns out to be an astronomical number and, moreover, when two messages are sent, if the second one is expressed as

$$W_2 = 2^{n_2} \tag{3-3}$$

then the combination of ways in which they can be sent is the product of W_1 and W_2:

$$W = W_1 W_2 = 2^{n_1} 2^{n_2} = 2^{n_1 + n_2} \tag{3-4}$$

An additive system would be handier. Taking logarithms, we have

$$\ln W_1 = n_1 \ln 2 \tag{3-5}$$

$$\ln W_2 = n_2 \ln 2 \tag{3-6}$$

$$\ln W = \ln W_1 + \ln W_2 = n_1 \ln 2 + n_2 \ln 2$$
$$= (n_1 + n_2) \ln 2 \tag{3-7}$$

Shannon suggested that we use not the log based on e nor the log based on 10, but rather the log based on 2; he called the result I.

$$I_1 = \log_2 W_1 = n_1 \log_2 2$$

But since $\log_2 2 = 1$, then (we can call $\log_2 2$ the "bit")

$$I_1 = n_1 \text{ bits} \tag{3-8}$$

$$I_2 = n_2 \text{ bits} \tag{3-9}$$

$$I_1 + I_2 = (n_1 + n_2) \text{ bits} \tag{3-10}$$

In the case of the English alphabet having 26 letters and one blank space, there are 27 symbols, and the number of distinctly different messages (without regard to meaning or value) which can be composed from n such symbols is

$$W = 27^n \tag{3-11}$$

If we take the log based on 2 of this, we can call it information I in bits.

$$I = \log_2 W = n \log_2 27 = n \, 4.76 \text{ bits} \qquad (3\text{-}12)$$

But the way to change $\log_{10} 27$ to $\log_2 27$ is to divide $\log_{10} 27$ by $\log_{10} 2$

$$I = \frac{n \log_{10} 27}{\log_{10} 2} \quad \text{or} \quad \frac{n \ln 27}{\ln 2} \qquad (3\text{-}13)$$

This last remark is not fundamental to information theory, but we will need it later.

3-3 A Priori Probability in the Usage of the English Alphabet

In actual usage the letters of the alphabet are not equally likely to occur, so they do not have equal a priori probabilities. Equations 3–11 and 3–12 apply only if the a priori probabilities are equal. We have shown for loaded dice and other objects that an equation different from Eq. 3–12 must be used.

$$\ln W = -n \sum_1^K p_j \ln p_j \qquad (3\text{-}14)$$

$$I = -n \sum p_j \log_2 p_j$$

Table 3–1 gives the values of p_j for the English alphabet taken directly from Brillouin.*

Table 3-1 THE RELATIVE FREQUENCY OF LETTERS

Symbol	p_j	Symbol	p_j
Blank	0.2	l	0.029
e	0.105	c	0.023
t	0.072	f and u	0.0225
o	0.0654	m	0.021
a	0.063	p	0.0175
n	0.059	y and w	0.012
i	0.055	g	0.011
r	0.054	b	0.0105
s	0.052	v	0.008
h	0.047	k	0.003
d	0.035	x	0.002
		j, q, z	0.001

The part of Eq. 3–14 including the summation sign is to be called

*Reference 5, p. 5.

the information per symbol in our alphabet. Using Table 3–1, one can compute the bits per letter from the equation

$$\frac{I}{n} = -\Sigma\, p_i\, \log_2\, p_i = 4.03$$

So information by this definition is additive, and we will find that entropy is also additive.

3-4   Information and Design

Let us go to a new phase of the discussion, that is, the extension of the ideas of information to design. This and other extensions have been made and applied to such problems as (for example) the information that can be transmitted per hour over a television set having a screen of known area when the time duration of each signal is known and also the area that each signal occupies on the screen. At least one author* likes to call some of these broader aspects of information by the name "description mechanics."

An illustration which at first seems trivial is as follows: Suppose a person were going to make a linear design of length L, using dots and dashes as the submotifs, and knowing that each submotif occupied a space ΔX in length. When the length L and ΔX are known, the number n of symbols is

$$n = \frac{L}{\Delta X} \tag{3–15}$$

The design might look like this:

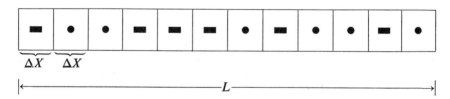

In this design, n can be either odd or even, and since the number of such designs is 2^n,

$$\ln\, W = n\, \ln\, 2, \qquad I = n \tag{3–16}$$

Now let us put a restriction upon the designer. The designer must start at the center and maintain the design symmetrical at all stages. At any moment that he is forced to stop adding submotifs the design

*Dan McLachlan, Jr., "The Role of Optics in Applying Correlation Functions to Pattern Recognition," *Journal of the Optical Society of America*, **52** (1962), 454–459.

must show symmetry, even if he is stopped after the first entry. The design could look like this:

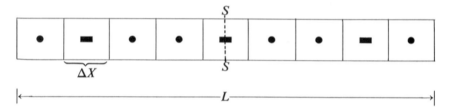

Now the number of symbols is still computed from Eq. 3–15,

$$n = \frac{L}{\Delta X}$$

but n must now be an odd number; that is what symmetry did to it. A good way to express an odd number is by the expression:

$$n_{\text{odd}} = 2n' + 1 = 2(n' + \tfrac{1}{2})$$

Also, one other thing has happened. Since the design is symmetrical, we cannot base the number of ways W on the total n. Symmetry fixes it so that when we arrange the symbols in, say, the left-hand side of the figure, we have no choice about the right-hand side, so W has to do with the motifs when n is an odd number. Eq. 3–16 takes the form

$$\ln W = \frac{2(n' + \tfrac{1}{2})}{2} \ln 2 = (n' + \tfrac{1}{2}) \ln 2$$

$$I = n' + \tfrac{1}{2} \tag{3–17}$$

Turning to the alphabet, if we knew the width ΔX of the space occupied by each letter typed by a typewriter and also knew the length L in inches of a printed message, we could get the number n of letters typed. Any line in this book can be used as an example. But if a symmetrical message of letters were sent, we have the same restrictions that we faced in the previous illustration. Although symmetrical messages that make sense are rare, at least one has been written. It was formulated by Napoleon while he was exiled at Elba. Capital letters neglected, it looks like this:

a
.
able was i ere i saw elba
.
a

Notice that this design (or sentence) has an odd number of letters, 19, and that r is the central one. If it were written from the center outward, its symmetry would be maintained at all stages. A mirror placed perpendicular to the paper at the dotted line *a-a* facing to the right would enable a person to write only the last half (correcting, of course, for the lack of symmetry of the individual letters). The possible number of such messages is

$$\ln W = (n' + \tfrac{1}{2}) \ln 27 \tag{3-18}$$

(compare with Eq. 3–17). Of course, we are not predicting how many make sense.

If one has a two-dimensional design that has a mirror symmetry and the *y* dimension is some function of *x* as shown in Fig. 3–1, then the area is

$$A = \int f(x) \, dx$$

$$n' = \frac{A}{2a} = \frac{\int fx dx}{2a}$$

where *n* is an odd number $(2n + 1)$ and *a* is the area $\Delta x \, \Delta y$, less than which either the designer or the observer is capable of discriminating.

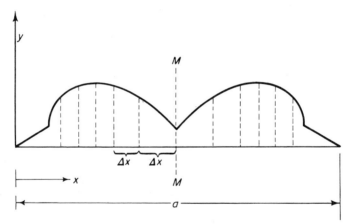

FIGURE **3-1**   A symmetrical figure divided into columns of variable width ΔX so that the areas of all columns are the same.

The kinds of symmetry possible in one-, two- and three-dimensional design have been worked out by group theorists and applied to X-ray crystallography and wave mechanics, but not quite in the manner that we are discussing the problem here, i.e., with the object of determining the possible number of significant submotifs which will fit into a known volume when the volume of each submotif is known. But there are two methods for solving for this number (call it *n*, *J*, or whatever is conventional).

3-5 Niels Bohr and Information Theory

Soon after Max Planck (1901)* presented the idea that energy came in discrete packets or quanta, Niels Bohr (1913)* applied this princi- ple to the Rutherford* model of the atom. The chief feature of Bohr's proposals was related to the idea of the "phase integral," a concept known to Boltzmann, Gibbs, and others. He proposed that when an electron goes in a circular orbit about an atom there is one restric- tion on the motion that is not encountered in the classical mechanics such as we use in astronomy, namely

$$\oint p_x \, dx = nh \qquad (3\text{-}19)$$

where $\oint$ means integration around the circuit, p_x is the momentum, and x the distance. The letter n is an integer, and h is Planck's con- stant 6.62×10^{-27}. Sommerfeld (1916)* extended this idea to elliptical orbits.

Although this all happened many years before information theory was ever heard about, we can now see that if we had a space called "phase space" having a coordinate in one direction p_x which is a function of the other coordinate x and if we were to integrate over it, we would have an area, just as we have in a two-dimensional design of coordinates x and y. If h were the area of a submotif, then the area $\int p \, dx$ would be some multiple n of the area of the submotif h. This is just what Eq. 3-19 says. We shall see that this n is the j in Eq. 2-43(c).

A paper entitled "Description Mechanics"† (all of the principles of which were borrowed from works by various authors of papers on information theory) introduced the thought that whereas the informa- tion content of a printed page was determined by the number of symbols (i.e., letters) typed, the information content of a picture depends upon the resolution $\Delta x \, \Delta y$ of the observer's eye or of the area of the blocks $\Delta x' \, \Delta y'$ used by the mosaic assembler (painter, basket weaver, or rug weaver, etc.), whichever area is the larger. The number n to be used in such equations as 3-14 is determined by the area of the picture divided by the area of resolution,

$$n = \frac{L_x L_y}{\Delta x \, \Delta y} \qquad (3\text{-}20)$$

*An elementary summary of the contributions of Planck, Bohr, Rutherford, and Sommerfeld is given in Ref. 31, pp. 330-372.
†Dan McLachlan, Jr., *Information and Control*, **1** (1958), 240-266.

where L_x and L_y are the dimensions of the picture. Of course, a resolution of $\Delta x \, \Delta y$ means that no point on the picture can be located with a greater areal accuracy than $\Delta x \, \Delta y$.

In 1925 Heisenberg* proposed the idea that the momentum and position of an electron could not be simultaneously determined with greater accuracy than is deduced from the equation,

$$\Delta p \, \Delta x = h \qquad (3\text{-}21)$$

This suggests that the subcell in phase space has an area h, and the more accurately we measure p or x, the more inaccurate is the other one measured. Equation 3–21 has nothing to do with human frailties; the different parts of the world do not register one another's positions or motions with any greater accuracy, whether we are talking about two planets or two nearby electrons.

In the meantime L. de Broglie proposed that the wavelength λ associated with a moving electron is (and experiments by Compton and others since have proved it)

$$\lambda = \frac{h}{p} \qquad (3\text{-}22)$$

and people working in optics knew that the best possible resolution is

$$\Delta x = \frac{\lambda}{2} \qquad (3\text{-}23)$$

All these findings fit into a beautiful picture, and some characteristics of atomic spectra were computed in agreements with experimental results. Then the Schrödinger wave equation (1926) came to the rescue and was successful where the Bohr model (Eq. 3–19) failed. Almost every text has a paragraph referring to the "breakdown of the old quantum theory." Nevertheless, we are going to use Eq. 3–19, and by adding to it the recent viewpoint of information theory (or description mechanics) we will show how the value of the elementary energy packet e and the function $f(j)$ can be arrived at, for use in Eqs. 2–43 (a–d).

3-6   The Particle in a Box†

Let us consider a particle in a tube of length a with closed ends and of such a diameter that the particle fits without friction but is forced to go in a straight line [Fig. 3–2(a)]. We assume that it has energy

*Reference 28 explains the Heisenberg principle.
†See, for example, Ref. 28, p. 41.

$E = \frac{1}{2}mv^2$, where m is mass and v is velocity. The particle goes then with a constant velocity and bounces back between the ends elastically, losing no energy either in transit or in the bouncing. In ordinary

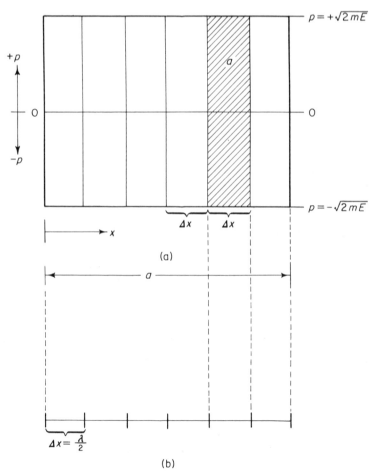

(a)

(b)

FIGURE 3-2   The particle in a tube. (a) Showing the limits of momentum and distance with a sample of the limiting areas a shaded. (b) Treating the problem as a one-dimensional figure using the concept that $\Delta X = \lambda/2$.

space this is a one-dimensional problem, but in phase space it is a rectangular area,* as shown in Fig. 3-2(a). The coordinates of this phase space are x and $p = mv$. The energy is

$$E = \frac{1}{2}mv^2 = \frac{1}{2}\frac{m^2 v^2}{m} = \frac{p^2}{2m}$$

*See, for example, Ref. 28, p. 41.

so the momentum is

$$p = \pm\sqrt{2mE}$$

The rectangle in phase space, as shown in Fig. 3–4(a) has dimensions a in the x direction and $2\sqrt{2mE}$ in the p direction. The area is

$$A = a2\sqrt{2mE}$$

If the subcells have area $\Delta x\ \Delta p = h$, then

$$2a\sqrt{2mE} = nh$$

Solving for E, we get

$$E_n = \frac{n^2 h^2}{8ma^2} \tag{3-24}$$

This equation is not under dispute, since it is the answer obtained from both the old quantum theory of Bohr and the newer work of Schrödinger, Heisenberg, and others. However, it must be remembered that this "design" in phase space has no symmetry because if the particle had no energy at all it could, with equal likelihood, be in any part of the space.

To convert to our previous symbolism used in Eqs. 2–43, let us change n to j and E_n to e_j; then our equation

$$e_j = ef(j) = \frac{h^2 j^2}{3ma^2} \tag{3-25}$$

so that the size of the packet of energy e referred to previously is

$$e = \frac{h^2}{8ma^2} \tag{3-26a}$$

and

$$f(j) = j^2 \tag{3-26b}$$

We could also have solved this problem as a one-dimensional design and consider only the coordinate x, if we had combined Eqs. 3–22 and 3–23 with the fact that $p = \sqrt{2mE}$.

$$\Delta x = \frac{\lambda}{2} = \frac{h}{2p} = \frac{h}{2\sqrt{2mE}} \tag{3-27a}$$

$$a = n\,\Delta x = \frac{nh}{2\sqrt{2mE}} \tag{3-27b}$$

or

$$E_n = \frac{n^2 h^2}{8ma^2} \tag{3-27c}$$

agreeing with Eq. 3–25.

In considering a orthorhombic box of sides a, b, and c, we get a six-dimensional phase space and three n values. Let us call them n_x, n_y, and n_z; then the energy is the sum of three equations like 3–27(c).

$$En_x n_y n_z = \frac{h^2}{8m}\left[\left(\frac{n_x}{a}\right)^2 + \left(\frac{n_y}{b}\right)^2 + \left(\frac{n_z}{c}\right)^2\right] \tag{3-28}$$

If the box is a cube, then $a = b = c$, and

$$E = \frac{h^2}{8ma^2}(n_x^2 + n_y^2 + n_z^2) \tag{3-29}$$

Since the sum of the squares of three integers is another integer, one might be tempted to assign it a value n' and let it go at that. But not any old n' will do, and this is misleading. (Later on we will discuss a phenomenon called degeneracy.)

We propose not to derive any of the principles of wave mechanics here, but rather to refer the reader to other texts.* All we will show is the one-dimensional wave equation of Schrödinger.

$$\frac{d^2 X}{dx^2} = -\frac{8\pi^2 m}{h^2}[W - V(x)]X \tag{3-30}$$

3-7 The Equation of a String†

Equation 3–30 looks very much like that portion of the equation of a vibrating string not involving the time. Since methods of solutions are similar, we discuss for a moment the vibrations of an elastic string of uniform linear density. The equation is

$$\rho\frac{d^2 y}{dt^2} = K\frac{d^2 y}{dx^2} \tag{3-31}$$

where ρ is the density, y the displacement from a straight line, and K is the tension on the string. We assume that the solution for y is a product of two other functions, X and T, where X is a function of x alone and T is a function of t alone:

$$y = X(x)T(t) \tag{3-32}$$

Differentiating, we get

$$\frac{dy}{dx} = T(t)\frac{dX}{dx} \quad \text{and} \quad \frac{d^2 y}{dx^2} = T(t)\frac{d^2 X}{dx^2}$$

$$\frac{dy}{dt} = X(t)\frac{dT}{dt} \quad \text{and} \quad \frac{d^2 y}{dt^2} = X(x)\frac{d^2 T}{dt^2} \tag{3-33}$$

*Reference 28, for example.

†For a good discussion of waves, see C. A. Coulson, *Waves* (London: Oliver and Boyd, 1947); and also Louis A. Pipes, *Applied Mathematics for Engineers and Physicists* (New York: McGraw-Hill, 1946), pp. 164–208.

Substituting Eq. 3–33 into Eq. 3–31, we have

$$\rho X \frac{d^2 T}{dt^2} = KT \frac{d^2 X}{dx^2} \tag{3–34a}$$

Now we divide by XT

$$\frac{\rho}{T} \frac{d^2 T}{dt^2} = \frac{K}{X} \frac{d^2 X}{dx^2} \tag{3–34b}$$

Now since the variables are separated, each side of the equation can be equal to a constant Q and solved separately:

$$\rho \frac{d^2 T}{dt^2} = -QT \tag{3–35a}$$

$$K \frac{d^2 X}{dx^2} = -QX \tag{3–35b}$$

In solving 3–35(a) we will let $(dT/dt) = V_t$ so that

$$\frac{d^2 T}{dt^2} = V_t \frac{dV_t}{dT}$$

Then Eq. 3–35(a) becomes

$$\rho V_t \frac{dV_t}{dT} = -QT \tag{3–36}$$

Integration gives

$$\tfrac{1}{2}\rho V_t^2 = -\tfrac{1}{2}QT^2 + \tfrac{1}{2}B \tag{3–37a}$$

where B is a constant.

$$V_t = \pm\sqrt{\frac{1}{\rho}(B - QT^2)} = \pm \frac{\sqrt{\dfrac{\rho}{Q}}}{\sqrt{\dfrac{B}{Q} - T^2}}$$

$$\equiv \frac{dT}{dt} \tag{3–37b}$$

Integrating Eq. 3–37(b), we have

$$\int_{t_0}^{t} dt = \int_{0}^{T} \pm \frac{\sqrt{\dfrac{\rho}{Q}}\,dT}{\sqrt{\dfrac{B}{Q} - T^2}} \rightarrow t - t_0 = \pm\sqrt{\frac{\rho}{Q}}\,\sin^{-1}\sqrt{\frac{Q}{B}}\,T \tag{3–38}$$

So

$$T(t) = \sqrt{\frac{B(t)}{Q}} \sin \sqrt{\frac{Q}{\rho}}(t - t_0) \tag{3–39a}$$

Similarly,

$$X(x) = \sqrt{\frac{B(x)}{Q}} \sin \sqrt{\frac{Q}{K}}(x - x_0) \tag{3–39b}$$

Putting these values into Eq. 3–32, we have

$$y = \sqrt{\frac{B(t)B(x)}{Q}} \sin \sqrt{\frac{Q}{\rho}} (x - x_0) \sin \sqrt{\frac{Q}{K}} (t - t_0) \qquad (3\text{–}40)$$

3-8 Boundary Conditions*

Now we can determine some of these constants by imposing boundary conditions. First we assume fixed origin at beginning of time so that $x_0 = t_0 = 0$, so the equation becomes

$$y = \sqrt{\frac{B_t B_x}{Q}} \sin \sqrt{\frac{Q}{\rho}} x \sin \sqrt{\frac{Q}{K}} t \qquad (3\text{–}41)$$

Next we know that the sine of an angle is less at all points than it is at $2\pi/4$ when it is unity. So when

$$\sqrt{\frac{Q}{\rho}} x = \sqrt{\frac{Q}{K}} t = \frac{\pi}{2}$$

$$y_{\max} = \sqrt{\frac{B_t B_x}{Q}} \qquad (3\text{–}42)$$

and we conclude that $\sqrt{B_t B_x / Q}$ is the amplitude and call it A.

$$y = A \sin \sqrt{\frac{Q}{\rho}} x \sin \sqrt{\frac{Q}{K}} t \qquad (3\text{–}43)$$

If the string is fixed (i.e., $y = 0$) at the far end (i.e., at a distance $x = a$) as well as at $x = 0$ for all time t, and if at certain instants at intervals of some time period τ the string is straight as well as at time $t = 0$, them

$$y = 0 = A \sin \sqrt{\frac{Q}{\rho}} a \sin \sqrt{\frac{Q}{K}} \tau \qquad (3\text{–}44)$$

which is only possible when

$$\sqrt{\frac{Q}{\rho}} a = \frac{2\pi n_x}{2} \quad \text{and} \quad \sqrt{\frac{Q}{K}} \tau = \frac{2\pi n_t}{2} \qquad (3\text{–}45a)$$

or

$$\sqrt{\frac{Q}{\rho}} = \frac{2\pi}{2a} \quad \text{and} \quad \sqrt{\frac{Q}{K}} = \frac{2\pi}{2\tau} \qquad (3\text{–}45b)$$

Substituting Eqs. 3–45(a–b) into Eq. 3–43 gives the particular solution,

$$y_{n_x n_y} = A_{n_x n_t} \sin \frac{2\pi n_x}{2a} x \sin \frac{2\pi n_t t}{2\tau} \qquad (3\text{–}46)$$

When we choose values for n_x and n_t we have the product of two

*For a broad practical look at boundary value problems, study Ref. 6.

sine wave* surfaces at right angles. Separate waves are shown for $n_x = 1$ and $n_y = 1$ in Figs. 3–3(a–b), and the product is shown in Fig. 3–3(c) for $n_x = 2$ and $n_t = 1$. This figure and Eq. 3–46 comply with our initial postulate of a product as stated in Eq. 3–32. If a person chooses an arbitrary value of t and runs a plane through this point on the t axis perpendicular to the xt plane and parallel with the x axis, he will find that the wave surface will cut the inserted plane surface along a simple sine wave of amplitude $A = A_{n_x n_t} \sin (2\pi n_t t / \tau)$. This is the amplitude of a "frozen" wave neglecting time as a variable, and its equation is

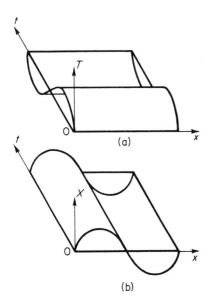

(a)

(b)

FIGURE **3-3 (a and b)** *Waves:* (a) A straight line through space waving with time. (b) A curve through space static through time (just a segment of a piece of corrugated sheet iron).

$$y_n = A \sin 2\pi \frac{n_x x}{2a} \qquad (3\text{–}47)$$

3-9 Similarities

There are several things we could do with Eq. 3–46 such as squaring it, integrating and setting the integral equal to unity (i.e., normalizing), etc., but all we are going to do is to point out the similarity between Eq. 3–47 and the solution that wave mechanists[†] find for Eq. 3–30, which is

$$X_n - \sqrt{\frac{2}{a}} \sin \frac{2\pi n_x x}{2a} \qquad (3\text{–}48)$$

for a particle in a channel of length a. The question of why it applies for a *free* particle is beyond the scope of this book. We shall just accept it, and refer the reader to other texts in which it has been treated.

As before, if we substitute the solution 3–48 back into Eq. 3–30, we determine the values of some of the parameters, particularly W_n, knowing $V(x) = 0$ for a free particle. First we must differentiate 3–48:

$$\frac{dX_n}{dx} = \frac{n\pi}{a} \sqrt{\frac{2}{a}} \cos \frac{n\pi x}{a} \qquad (3\text{–}49a)$$

*A discussion of nonsinusoidal waves is given by Dan McLachlan, Jr., "Unified Treatment of the Vibrating Arm," *American Journal of Physics*, **25** (1957), 228.

†Reference 28.

$$\frac{d^2 X_n}{dx^2} = -\frac{n^2 \pi^2}{a^2} \sqrt{\frac{2}{a}} \sin \frac{2\pi nx}{2a} \qquad (3\text{-}49b)$$

These expressions applied to Eq. 3–30 give

$$-\frac{n^2 \pi^2}{a^2} \sqrt{\frac{2}{a}} \sin \frac{\pi nx}{a} = -\frac{8\pi^2 m}{h^2} W \sqrt{\frac{2}{a}} \sin \frac{n\pi x}{a}$$

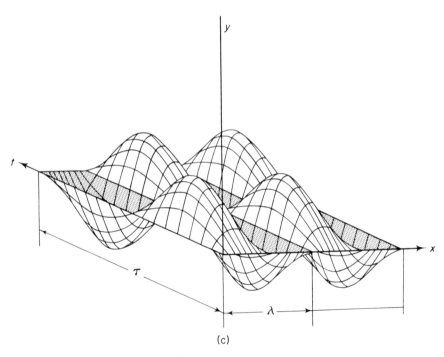

(c)

FIGURE **3-3(c)** *Waves:* The product of the waves in Figures 3–3(a) and 3–3(b) resulting in a standing wave of period τ and wavelength λ.

Cancelling out $\pi^2 \sqrt{2/a} \sin \pi nx/a$ on both sides gives

$$\frac{n^2}{a^2} = 8 \frac{m W_n}{h^2}$$

or

$$W_n = \frac{n^2 h^2}{8ma^2} \qquad \text{(cf. Eq. 3–24)}$$

3-10   The Perfect Gas*

A perfect gas is defined as a large number n of point particles, having
an energy $e_j = \frac{1}{2} mVj^2$ filling a volume V, while the particles (or
atoms) themselves occupy no volume at all; since they do not attract
one another or the walls, the potential energy is zero except at the
walls, where the potential energy would go to ∞ if they could pene-
trate time. Thus a perfect gas is not just one particle in a box as
was discussed above, but a large number n (a statistically adequate
number) of such particles, each obeying Eq. 3–25. Since each of the
many particles has its own energy of translation at velocity v_j at any
particular instant, and can transmit it (or exchange it) with any or
all others, there is an equilibrium set up in the energy exchange.
There is a minimum size of the energy packet e, just as there were
sizes of the minimum change in the limousine and theater problems,
and this size for a perfect gas is given in Eq. 3–26(a) from quantum
mechanics. The amount of energy that any atom has at any one time
is given in Eq. 3–25 dependent upon the rule of rates $f(j)$, which for
a perfect gas is $f(j) = j^2$. So the problem is similar to the squared-
rate theater (see Sec. 2–9), and we have to satisfy three equations: the
conservation of the number of particles,

$$n = \sum_j n_j$$

the conservation of energy,

$$E = \sum_j e_j n_j \qquad\qquad \text{(cf. Eqs. 2–3a, b, c)}$$

and the maximization of the number of ways

$$W = \frac{n!}{\pi(n_j!)}$$

Since the perfect gas problem is identical to the squared-rate theater
problem, we can use Eqs. 2–46(a–c) without alteration, except for
symbolism. Replacing the j term, which applied to one degree of
freedom, by that for three degrees as we did in Eq. 3–28, we get for
the partition function Q the equation

$$Q = \sum_{n_x=0}^{L_x} \sum_{n_y=0}^{L_y} \sum_{n_z=0}^{L_z} e^{-h^2/(2\bar{e}8m)\,[(n_x/a)^2 + (n_y/b)^2 + (n_z/c)^2]} \qquad (3\text{–}50)$$

This can be approximated by an integration, since e^{-ax^2} is such a
rapidly descending function and the intervals are close together, and
we can go to ∞ instead of L.

*Reference 16, pp. 88–90, and Ref. 26, p. 178.

$$Q \doteq \int_0^\infty \int_0^\infty \int_0^\infty e^{-h^2/(2\bar{e}8m)\,[(n_x^2/a^2)+(n_y^2/b^2)+(n_z^2/c^2)]}\,dn_x dn_y dn_z \tag{3-51}$$

and this is like the equation

$$y = y_1 y_2 y_3 = \int_0^\infty e^{-a_1^2 x_1^2}\,dx_1 \int_0^\infty e^{-a_2^2 x_2^2}\,dx_2 \int_0^\infty e^{-a_3^2 x_3^2}\,dx_1\,dx_2\,dx_3$$

which, according to Peirce's tables, p. 68, is

$$y = \frac{\sqrt{\pi}}{2a_1}\frac{\sqrt{\pi}}{2a_2}\frac{\sqrt{\pi}}{2a_3} = \frac{\pi^{3/2}}{8abc}$$

Since $abc = V$, the volume, if we assume a cube, is

$$Q = \left(\frac{2\bar{e}\pi 2m}{h^2}\right)^{3/2} V \tag{3-52}$$

and

$$n_j = \frac{n}{Q}\,e^{-h^2/(2\bar{e}8m)\,[(n_x^2/a^2)+(n_y^2/b^2)+(n_z^2/c^2)]} \tag{3-53}$$

Equations 3-52 and 3-53 are the three-dimensional analogs of Eqs. 2-46(a) and (c). Much could be done with Eqs. 3-52 and 3-53 if we knew how to evaluate the term $\bar{e}$ representing the average energy per particle. Before we plunge into this, it is desirable to discuss three other topics: (1) equilibrium, (2) the kinetic theory of gases, and (3) the meaning of temperature.

3-11   Equilibrium

We have discussed three kinds of theaters based on the admission rates for the various L sections: the flat-rate theater, the linear-rate theater, and the squared-rate theater, and found that for one physical system, the perfect gas is almost directly analogous to the squared-rate theater. The general equation for the distribution is (see Eq. 2-43c)

$$n_j = \frac{ne^{-ef(j)/2\bar{e}}}{Q} \tag{3-54}$$

We already know from Eqs. 2-44(a)—2-46(c) that e is different for different systems and so is $f(j)$ by definition; consequently Q must be, and is, different. Now we wish to investigate $\bar{e}$ to see how it varies with the scale of rates.

Suppose we had two theaters, 1 and 2, sitting side by side but having different rate functions $f_1(j)$ and $f_2(j)$ and different minima of change e_1 and e_2. The customers with their dollars can go from one to the other at will, so that the two theaters will come into equilibrium as a consequence of the maximization of the grand or combined number of ways

$$W = W_1 W_2$$

In the first theater,

$$W_1 = \frac{n_1!}{\prod_j (n_{1j}!)} = \frac{n_1!}{\prod \left(\frac{ne^{-ef(j)/2\bar{e}}}{Q} ! \right)} \tag{3-55a}$$

and in the second theater,

$$W_2 = \frac{n_2!}{\prod (n_{2j}!)} = \frac{n_2!}{\prod \left[\left(\frac{ne^{-e_2 f_2(j)/2\bar{e}_2}}{Q_1} \right) ! \right]} \tag{3-55b}$$

and

$$W_{12} = W_1 W_2 = \frac{n_1! \, n_2!}{\prod \left(\frac{n}{Q_1} \exp \frac{-e_1 f_1(j)}{2\bar{e}_1} ! \right) \prod \left(\frac{n}{Q_2} \exp \frac{-e_2 f_2(j)}{2\bar{e}_2} ! \right)} \tag{3-56}$$

We can reduce Eq. 3-56 to a simpler form after taking a diversion. For brevity let (as in Eq. 2-40)

$$e^{-e_1 f_1(j)/2\bar{e}} = e^{-e_j/2\bar{e}} \tag{3-57}$$

so that

$$n_j = \frac{n}{Q} e^{-e_j/2\bar{e}} \tag{3-58}$$

Using Stirling's approximation $m! \doteq m^m$, we have

$$n_{1j}! = \left(\frac{n_1}{Q_1} e^{-e_{1j}/2\bar{e}_1} \right)^{(n_1/Q_1)} e^{-e_{1j}/2\bar{e}_1} \tag{3-59}$$

or

$$\ln n_{1j}! = \frac{n_1}{Q_1} e^{-e_{1j}/2\bar{e}_1} \ln \frac{n_1}{Q_1} - \frac{n_1}{Q_1} e^{-e_{1j}/2\bar{e}_1} \ln e^{-e_{1j}/2\bar{e}_1} \tag{3-60}$$

and

$$\ln \pi n_{1j}! = \frac{n_1}{Q_1} \ln \frac{n_1}{Q_1} \sum e^{-e_{1j}/2\bar{e}_1} + \frac{n_1}{Q_1} \sum \frac{e_{1j}}{2\bar{e}_{1j}} e^{-e_{1j}/2\bar{e}_1} \tag{3-61}$$

since

$$\sum e^{-e_{1j}/2\bar{e}} = Q_1 \quad \text{and} \quad \sum \frac{n_1}{Q_1} e^{-e_{1j}/2\bar{e}_1} = \sum e_{1j} n_{1j} = E_1$$

$$\ln \prod n_{1j}! = \frac{n_1}{Q_1} \ln \frac{n_1}{Q_1} Q + \frac{E_1}{\bar{e}_1}$$

$$= n_1 \ln \frac{n_1}{Q_1} + \frac{E_1}{\bar{e}_1} \tag{3-62}$$

Then

$$\prod n_{1j}! = \left(\frac{n_1}{Q_1}\right)^{n_1} e^{-E_1/2\bar{e}} \tag{3-63}$$

and the same procedure applies to $\prod(n_{2j})!$. Equation 3-63 now simplifies Eq. 3-56.

$$W_{12} = W_1 W_2 = \frac{n_1! \, n_2!}{\left(\dfrac{n_1}{Q_1}\right)^{n_1} e^{-E_1/2\bar{e}_1} \left(\dfrac{n_2}{Q_2}\right)^{n_2} e^{-E_2/2\bar{e}_2}} \tag{3-64}$$

If W_{12} is really at its maximum value, then using the reasoning described by Gurney, we should be able to take a small amount of gate receipts Δe from one of these theaters and add it to the other without changing W_{12} much. The new number of ways is

$$W_{12}^* = \frac{n_1! \, n_2!}{\left(\dfrac{n_1}{Q_1}\right)^{n_1} \exp \dfrac{-(E_1 - \Delta e)}{2\bar{e}_1} \left(\dfrac{n_2}{Q_2}\right)^{n_2} \exp \dfrac{-(E_2 + \Delta e)}{2\bar{e}_2}} \tag{3-65}$$

If W_{12} has not changed much

$$\frac{W_{12}^*}{W_{12}} = \frac{\exp \dfrac{-E_1}{2\bar{e}_1} \exp \dfrac{-E_2}{2\bar{e}_2}}{\exp \dfrac{-(E_1 - \Delta e)}{2\bar{e}_1} \exp - \dfrac{E_2 + \Delta e}{2\bar{e}_2}} = e^{-\Delta e/2\bar{e}_1} \, e^{\Delta e/2\bar{e}_2} \doteq 1$$

or

$$\exp\left[-\Delta e\left(\frac{1}{2\bar{e}_1} - \frac{1}{2\bar{e}_2}\right)\right] \doteq 1 \tag{3-66}$$

If Δe is not zero, then $(1/2\bar{e}_1) - (1/2\bar{e}_2)$ must be zero. Therefore,

$$\bar{e}_1 = \bar{e}_2 \tag{3-67}$$

Equation 3-67 is quite astounding because it implies that all theaters that are in equilibrium have the same average payments at the ticket window per patron or, in physical systems, the same average energy per degree of freedom. If a man in theater management just knew *all* about a theater in any one of the rate scales, he could set a very small theater of that type next to any new enterprise and use it as a thermometer, so to speak.

In physical systems there is one that we think we understand, and that is the perfect gas with its squared-rate properties.

3-12 The Temperature Dilemma

There is a sort of a weird paradox connecting temperature and entropy. The smallest child develops a personal familiarity with temperature beginning with the first burning of his fingers on a hot object, but in spite of his extreme talents for creating chaos, the concept of entropy seems to be hopelessly beyond him until he is well educated. Then after he is educated, temperature becomes a puzzle and stays that way for most people.

Long before people cared to understand temperature as connected with atomic phenomena, they nevertheless wanted to put numbers on it for comparison. If a very cold day in winter were called 0 deg and a very hot day in summer were called 100 deg and the interval between were marked off into 100 parts, we would have something resembling Fahrenheit. If that were all we had, temperature measurements would be slowed up by the infrequency of occurrence of calibrated days and the inability to recognize one very accurately when it arrived. But it was long ago noticed that objects expanded as they and their surroundings were warmed. The length of the objects of higher expansion could be marked off against some reference object that appeared to expand infinitesimally, i.e., zero. The statement that an object expands linearly with temperature (at this stage) is wrapped up in the definition of temperature and only means that one has gained by observation the knowledge that any two expandable objects, such as a rod of copper and a tube of grain alcohol, maintain the same ratio,

$$R_{12} = \frac{\Delta L_1/L_1}{\Delta L_2/L_2}$$

throughout a limited warming and cooling cycle.

Finally it was found that at one atmosphere pressure the melting point of ice and the boiling point of water, with reference to the expansion of other objects, were pretty constant and reliable. Using the melting point of ice as 0 and the boiling point of water as 100 and dividing the interval into 100 points is the basis of the centigrade scale. Temperatures below the freezing point of ice were considered negative, but it became apparent eventually that nothing (even a perfect gas whose atoms occupy zero volume at rest) can keep on shrinking indefinitely after it has shrunken to zero. Lord Kelvin, who introduced the idea of absolute zero at 273 deg below 0 deg centigrade, still clung to the centigrade scale in "degrees Kelvin." Of course, Kelvin's work could not have been so quantitative without some contributions by at least two men who presented the Avogadro number, 6.02×10^{23}, and the Boltzmann constant, 1.38×10^{-16} ergs per degree per atom.

In order to understand the meaning of temperature, we must know some of the things Boltzmann knew. Determining temperature by putting something expandable against it is practically useful, but it produces no more basic understanding than was obtained by the man who owned a huge chicken house full of fighting cocks in which occasionally an uproarious free-for-all broke out. To determine numerically the degree of violence going on, he released a calibrated bantam rooster inside for three minutes with a string on his leg and got his desired number by counting the missing feathers. Just as the study of the social life among our feathered friends requires a more refined technique, the understanding of temperature first requires reference to a perfect gas, because it was the first physical state of matter to which kinetic theory was thoroughly applied.

3-13   The Kinetic Theory of the Perfect Gas*

Let us suppose that we have a box that is cubic in shape containing N atoms of the perfect-gas type (see Fig. 3–4), each atom having an average energy in the x direction of $\bar{e}_x$, in the y direction $\bar{e}_y$, and in the z direction $\bar{e}_z$. The total energy is

$$\bar{e} = \bar{e}_x + \bar{e}_y + \bar{e}_z = \frac{E}{N} \qquad (3\text{--}68)$$

where E is the total energy of the N atoms and N is Avogadro's number. All this energy is kinetic and none of it is potential.

$$\bar{e} = 3\bar{e}_x = 3(\tfrac{1}{2}m\bar{v}_x^2) \qquad (3\text{--}69)$$

where m is the mass of the atom and $\bar{v}_x$ is the average velocity in the x direction. The average momentum is $\bar{M}_x$ and the change in momentum when an atom hits a wall is $2\bar{M}_x$ because of its return in the opposite direction without loss of velocity.

$$\Delta \bar{M}_x = 2\bar{M}_x = 2m\bar{v}_x = 2m\sqrt{\frac{2\bar{e}x}{m}} \qquad (3\text{--}70)$$

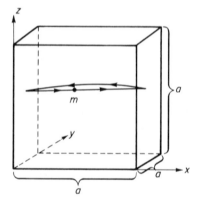

FIGURE **3-4** A cube of dimensions a with a particle of mass m in it.

Solving for $\bar{v}_x$ from Eq. 3–69 and substituting it into 3–70 gives

$$\Delta \bar{M}_x = 2\sqrt{2m\bar{e}_x} \qquad (3\text{--}71)$$

The average number of collisions per second against a wall is $\bar{\nu}$.

$$\bar{\nu} = \frac{\bar{v}_x}{2a} = \frac{1}{2a}\sqrt{\frac{2\bar{e}_x}{m}} \qquad (3\text{--}72)$$

since $2a$ is the distance travelled in going to the opposite wall and returning.

*Reference 14, pp. 27–32.

The momentum change per second is *force*, which, combining Eqs. 3–70 and 3–72, gives

$$f_x = \Delta \bar{M}_x \bar{v}_x = 2m\sqrt{\frac{2\bar{e}_x}{m}}\frac{1}{2a}\sqrt{\frac{2\bar{e}_x}{m}}$$

$$= \frac{2\bar{e}_x}{a} \tag{3–73}$$

Force per unit area is pressure p.

$$p = \frac{f_x}{a^2} = \frac{2\bar{e}_x}{a^3} = \frac{2\bar{e}_x}{V} \tag{3–74}$$

where V is volume. So per atom (using Eq. 3–68), we have

$$pV = 2\bar{e}_x = \frac{2\bar{e}}{3} = \frac{2}{3}\left(\frac{1}{2}mv^2\right) \tag{3–75}$$

If one were to take a volume of a perfect gas at a pressure of one dyne and heat it until it expanded an amount to show a difference of one degree as agreed upon by the divisions marked off on a centigrade or Kelvin scale, and if he calorimetrically measured the heat energy required to cause this much expansion, then he could say (setting $p = 1$ in Eq. 3–75) that

$$\Delta V = V_2 - V_1 = \tfrac{2}{3}(\bar{e}_2 - \bar{e}_1) \equiv 1 \text{ deg}$$

If it were found experimentally that $\bar{e}_2 - \bar{e}_1 = 1.38053 \times 10^{-16}$ ergs per degree per atom, we could call this factor k the Boltzmann constant. If N atoms were used, we would have the ergs per degree per mol, i.e., the gas constant R.

$$R = NK = 6.02257 \times 10^{23} \times 1.38053 \times 10^{-16}$$

$$= 8.31432 \times 10^7 \text{ ergs per degree per mol} \tag{3–76}$$

So combining Eqs. 3–65 and 3–70, we find

$$pV = kT = (\tfrac{2}{3})\bar{e}$$

and

$$\bar{e} = \tfrac{3}{2}kT \quad \text{(for three degrees of freedom)}$$

So, in a perfect gas the energy per degree of freedom is

$$\bar{e} = \frac{kT}{2} \tag{3–77}$$

Therefore, we have, in all equations (for physical systems) in which $2\bar{e}$ appears, only to replace it by kT. The general equation 2–43(c) for the distribution of energy now becomes

$$n_j = ne^{-ef(j)/kT} \tag{3–78}$$

for all systems, and all that is required is to determine from quantum mechanics the values of the approximate unit e and the function $f(j)$. For example, the partition function for a perfect gas is as determined by Eq. 3–52.

$$Q = \left(\frac{2\pi mkT}{h^2}\right)^{3/2} V \tag{3-79}$$

and the distribution law is (see Eq. 3–53)

$$n_j = \frac{n}{Q} \exp - \frac{h^2}{8mkT}\left[\left(\frac{n_x}{a}\right)^2 + \left(\frac{n_y}{b}\right)^2 + \left(\frac{n_z}{c}\right)^2\right]$$

$$= \frac{n}{V}\left(\frac{h^2}{2\pi mkT}\right)^{3/2} e^{-e_j/kT} \tag{3-80}$$

3-14 The Harmonic Oscillator*

A harmonic oscillator can be illustrated by a mass m which is permitted to move in a straight line along the x coordinate to or from a point at $x = 0$, but in so doing experiences a force which is proportional to the displacement and the direction; this force is back toward the origin; i.e., $f(x) = -Kx$. The force is equal to mass multiplied by acceleration; i.e., $f = ma$. The potential energy V is obtained by integration,

$$V(x) = \int_0^x f(x)\,dx = \int_0^x Kx\,dx = \left[\frac{Kx^2}{2}\right]_0^x$$

$$= \frac{Kx^2}{2} \tag{3-81}$$

when $x = x(\max)$; $V(x)$ is equal to the total energy E, and the kinetic energy is zero; at other positions the kinetic energy is equal to

$$\frac{1}{2}mv^2 = \frac{1}{2}m\left(\frac{dx}{dt}\right)^2 = E - \frac{1}{2}Kx^2$$

where v is the velocity, or since $p = mv$ (the momentum),

$$\frac{p^2}{2m} = E - \frac{1}{2}Kx^2 \tag{3-82}$$

or

$$\frac{p^2}{2m} + \frac{1}{2}Kx^2 = E$$

which is analogous to the equation of an ellipse:

$$ax^2 + by^2 = c$$

In phase space, where the coordinates are p and x, the ellipse looks

*See Ref. 18, pp. 73–76, and Ref. 36 in general.

as in Fig. 3–5, where the semi-axes are $X_{max} = \sqrt{2E/K}$ and $P_{max} = \sqrt{2mE}$.

It is known that the area of an ellipse is πab, where a and b are the semi-axes. So the area of the ellipse in phase space is

$$A = \pi X_{max} P_{max} = \pi\sqrt{\frac{2E}{K}}\sqrt{2mE} = 2\pi E\sqrt{\frac{m}{K}} \tag{3-83}$$

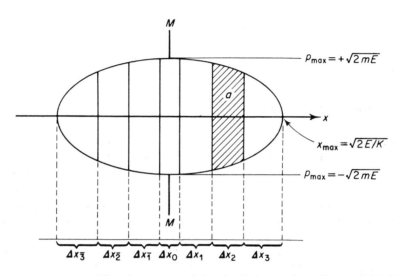

FIGURE 3-5   The phase space of the simple harmonic oscillator, divided into equal areas $a = h$ and the limits shown for the semi-major and semi-minor axes as they are related to the maximum momentum and maximum displacement. Notice that the boundaries of the areas a are marked perpendicular to the X axis to show that their width, $\Delta X = \lambda/2$, varies with momentum p. In Bohr's original diagrams, the areas were marked concentrically; he did not consider deBroglie's connection between λ and momentum, because this latter discovery came later.

Since this figure is symmetrical, we need only consider half this area. As in Sec. 3–4, when considering one-half of this area and after dividing it by a small subarea $a = h$, we expect to get an odd number n'.

$$\frac{A}{2}\frac{1}{a} = \frac{2\pi E\sqrt{m/K}}{2h} = n' = (2n + 1) \tag{3-84}$$

or

$$E = \frac{1}{\pi}\sqrt{\frac{K}{m}}\, h(2n + 1) \tag{3-85}$$

This problem of the harmonic oscillator is similar to the problems discussed in Sec. 3–7, because its differential equation is

$$f = ma = \frac{m\,d^2 x}{dt^2} = -Kx \tag{3-86}$$

and the solution is of the form

$$x = X_{max} \sin \sqrt{\frac{K}{m}}\, t = X_{max} \sin \frac{2\pi t}{\tau}$$

$$= X_{max} \sin 2\pi\nu t \tag{3-87}$$

where τ is the period and ν is the frequency which is

$$\nu = \frac{1}{2\pi}\sqrt{\frac{K}{m}} \tag{3-88}$$

or

$$\frac{1}{\pi}\sqrt{\frac{K}{m}} = 2\nu \tag{3-89}$$

When this result is substituted into Eq. 3–85,

$$E = \frac{h\nu}{2}(2n + 1) = \left(n + \frac{1}{2}\right)h\nu \tag{3-90}$$

For an oscillator free to vibrate about a point in three dimensions,

$$E = E_x + E_y + E_z$$
$$= (n_x + \tfrac{1}{2})h\nu + (n_y + \tfrac{1}{2})h\nu + (n_z + \tfrac{1}{2})h\nu$$
$$= (n_x + n_y + n_z)h\nu + \tfrac{3}{2}h\nu \tag{3-91}$$

Since the sum of these integers is also an integer, we could just call this integer a new n and let it go at that. But this is dangerous, and since the function $e^{-\epsilon j/\ell}$ does not descend as fast nor have as small steps as $e^{-\epsilon j^2/\ell}$, we cannot approximate the summations (which are to follow) by integration as we did in dealing with the particles in a box in simulating a perfect gas. At this time we should say something about degeneracy, but before doing so, let us add one more thought for completeness.

3-15 Degeneracy and the Harmonic Oscillator

In dealing with a set of three numbers such as

$$n_x + n_y + n_z = n \tag{3-92}$$

we once more (as in Sec. 1–14) have to deal with an equation that is analogous to

$$x + y + z = c$$

which we have shown to be the equation of a plane like *ABC* in Fig. 1–8(a) with intersections as shown in Fig. 1–8(b). A smaller version of Fig. 1–8(b) is shown in Fig. 3–6. Every intersection corresponds to a possible combination of integers n_x, n_y, n_z; and, by actual count, Fig. 3–6 has 28 intersections (or a degeneracy of 28),

$$W = \frac{(6 + 3 - 1)!}{(3 - 1)!\,6!} = \frac{8!}{2!\,6!} = 28$$

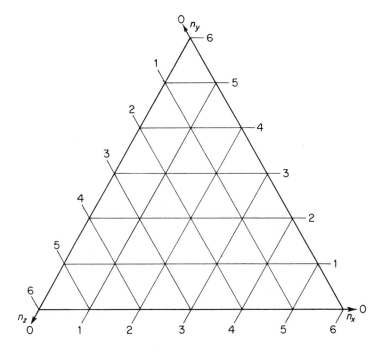

FIGURE **3-6**   A construction for the computation of degeneracy of a harmonic oscillator.

It is of interest that if one has a *D*-dimensional space and a number *n* such that

$$n_1 + n_2 + n_3 + \cdots + n_j + \cdots + n_D = n$$

then

$$W = \frac{(n + D - 1)!}{(D - 1)!\,n!} \tag{3–93}$$

When we have a three-dimensional harmonic oscillator, and by spectroscopy or other means, we can find an *n* which we know can be composed of three additive numbers n_x, n_y, and n_z as in Eq. 3–92, then we have a degeneracy ω which can be computed by putting $D = 3$ in Eq. 3–93.

$$W = \frac{(n + 3 - 1)!}{(3 - 1)! \, n!} = \frac{(n + 2)!}{2(n!)} = \frac{1}{2}(n + 2)(n + 1) \qquad (3\text{–}94)$$

3-16   The Partition Function with Degeneracy*

In view of this, the equation for the partition function Q as previously stated throughout these pages must be modified as follows:

$$Q = \sum_j \omega_j e^{-e_j/2\varepsilon} = \sum_j \omega_j e^{-e_j/kT} \qquad (3\text{–}95)$$

For the harmonic oscillator we cannot *integrate* and hope for good accuracy as we did in dealing with the perfect gas; we must *sum*.

$$Q = \sum \tfrac{1}{2}(j + 2)(j + 1)e^{-ef(j)/kT}$$

From Eq. 3–91 we see that $e = h\nu$ and $f(j) = (j + \tfrac{3}{2})$.

$$Q = \sum_j \tfrac{1}{2}(j + 2)(j + 1)e^{-h\nu(j + 3/2)/kT}$$

$$= e^{-3/2(h\nu/kT)} \sum_{j=0}^{\infty} \left[\frac{(j + 2)(j + 1)}{2} e^{-jh\nu/kT} \right]$$

$$= e^{-3/2(h\nu/kT)} \left[\frac{(0 + 2)(0 + 1)}{2} e^0 + \frac{(1 + 2)(1 + 1)}{2} e^{h\nu} + \cdots \right]$$

$$= e^{-3/2(h\nu/kT)} [1 + \tfrac{6}{2} e^{-h\nu/kT} + \tfrac{12}{2} e^{-2h\nu/kT} + \tfrac{20}{2} e^{-3h\nu/kT} + \cdots]$$

$$= e^{-3/2(h\nu/kT)} [1 + 3(e^{-h\nu/kT}) + 6(e^{-h\nu/kT})^2 + 10(e^{-h\nu/kT})^3 + \cdots]$$

Letting $e^{-h\nu/kT} = x$, we have

$$Q = e^{-3/2(h\nu/kT)} [1 + 3x + 6x^2 + 10x^3 + \cdots]$$

$$= e^{-3/2(h\nu/kT)} \left[1 + 3x + \frac{3(3 + 1)}{2!} x^2 + \frac{3(3 + 1)(3 + 2)}{3!} x^3 + \cdots \right]$$

which, when compared with Eq. 816 of p. 97 of Peirce's tables is equivalent to

$$Q_v = e^{-3/2(h\nu/kT)}(1 - x)^{-3}$$

$$= \frac{e^{-3/2(h\nu/kT)}}{(1 - e^{-h\nu/kT})^3} = \left(\frac{e^{-1/2(h\nu/kT)}}{1 - e^{-h\nu/kT}} \right)^3 \qquad (3\text{–}96)$$

Such a partition function could pertain to the stretching vibrations of a diatomic molecule or to an atom vibrating about a lattice site in a perfect crystal, providing, of course, that the amplitudes of vibration were not too great for the assumption of *linear* restoring forces to be applicable.

*References 16 and 32; also, Ref. 26, p. 188.

3-17 Degeneracy in Rotating Molecules

Degeneracy is not an exceptional occurrence in real physical systems. The diatomic molecule that is rotating without vibrating is treated in wave mechanics as a rotating dumbbell with the masses of the knobs not necessarily equal. It is found in this case that the energy of the jth level is

$$e_j = \frac{h^2}{8\pi I} J(J+1) \tag{3-97}$$

and the degeneracy is $(2J+1)$. So the partition function is

$$Q_r = \sum_J (2J+1)e^{-(h^2J/8\pi I)(J+1)/kT} \tag{3-98}$$

In these equations, I is the moment of inertia (see Fig. 3-4).

$$I = m_1 r_1^2 + m_2 r_2^2 \tag{3-99}$$

where m_1 is the mass of one particle and m_2 is the mass of the other, and r_1 and r_2 are their respective distances from the center of gravity. Since the center of mass must be constant,

$$r_1 = \frac{m_2}{m_1 + m_2} r \quad \text{and} \quad r_2 = \frac{m_1}{m_1 + m_2} r \tag{3-100}$$

Introducing Eq. 3-100 into Eq. 3-99 gives

$$I = \frac{m_1 m_2}{m_1 + m_2} r^2 \tag{3-101}$$

Some people like to abbreviate Eq. 3-101 by letting $m_1 m_2/(m_1 + m_2) = \mu$, and calling it the reduced mass; then

$$I = \mu r^2 \tag{3-102}$$

Inspection of Eq. 3-97 shows that our terms (see Eq. 3-1) e and $f(j)$ for the rotating rigid diatomic molecule are $h^2/8\pi I$ and $J(J+1)$, respectively.

3-18 Energy and Heat Capacity

By now the reader is no doubt eager to see something that looks like physical chemistry. In compliance with this desire we will now discuss the energies and heat capacities of (a) a perfect gas, (b) an assemblage of independent three-dimensional oscillators, and (c) an ideal diatomic molecular gas.

(a) *The perfect gas.* The energy of a mole of perfect gas has been shown in Sec. 3–13 to be

$$E = \tfrac{3}{2} NKT = \tfrac{3}{2} RT \qquad (3\text{-}103)$$

When R is expressed in calories per degree per mole instead of ergs it has the approximate value of 2 calories.

$$E = (\tfrac{3}{2})2T = 3T = PV$$

The heat capacity at constant volume is

$$C_v = \left(\frac{\partial E}{\partial T}\right)_v = 3 \text{ cal} \qquad (3\text{-}104)$$

(b) *Independent harmonic oscillators.* Let us suppose that we have an assemblage of N independent oscillators, each uncoupled with its neighbors but still capable of exchanging energy packets (by radiation or other means) so that the distribution of energy between them is such that the number of ways W that the energy can be distributed is a maximum. Einstein did this the first time by computing the energy of N linear harmonic oscillators and then, assuming that there are three degrees of freedom, he multiplied by three.

$$E = 3 \sum e_j N_j = 3 \sum \left(j + \frac{1}{2}\right) h\nu \left[\frac{Ne^{-h\nu(j+1/2)/kT}}{\sum e^{-h\nu(j+1/2)/kT}}\right] \qquad (3\text{-}105)$$

The summation in the denominator will be recognized as the partition function of a linear harmonic oscillator. Notice also that in dealing with one dimension, one does not have to worry about degeneracy. Separating this equation into two parts, we have

$$E = 3N h\nu \left[\frac{\sum j e^{-h\nu(j+1/2)/kT}}{\sum e^{-h\nu(j+1/2)/kT}} + \frac{\tfrac{1}{2}\sum e^{-h\nu(j+1/2)/kT}}{\sum e^{-h\nu(j+1/2)/kT}}\right] \qquad (3\text{-}106)$$

The term $\tfrac{1}{2}$ cancels in the exponent of the first term on the right-hand side of this equation and in the second term all cancels to $\tfrac{1}{2}$. So

$$E = \frac{3}{2} N h\nu \left[1 + 2\frac{\sum j e^{-h\nu j/kT}}{\sum e^{-h\nu j/kT}}\right] \qquad (3\text{-}107)$$

The term $\sum j e^{-h\nu j/kT}$ has the form*

$$x(1 + 2x + 3x^2 + 4x^3 + \cdots + jx^{j-1} + \cdots) = \sum jx^j = \frac{x}{(1-x)^2}$$

where $x = e^{-h\nu/kT}$ and the term $\sum e^{-h\nu j/kT}$ has the form*

$$(1 + x + x^2 + x^3 + \cdots) = \frac{1}{1-x}$$

So Eq. 3–107 reduces to

*Reference 36, p. 31; Ref. 26, p. 127; and Peirce's tables, p. 98, Eq. 826.

$$E = \frac{3}{2} Nh\nu \left[1 + \frac{2e^{-h\nu/kT}}{(1 - e^{-h\nu/kT})^2} (1 - e^{-h\nu/kT}) \right]$$

$$= \frac{3}{2} Nh\nu + \frac{3Nh\nu e^{-h\nu/kT}}{1 - e^{-h\nu/kT}}$$

$$= \frac{3}{2} Nh\nu + \frac{3Nh\nu}{e^{h\nu/kT} - 1} \tag{3-108}$$

To get C_v, we differentiate with respect to T and obtain

$$C_v = 3Nk \left(\frac{h\nu}{kT}\right)^2 \frac{e^{h\nu/kT}}{(e^{h\nu/kT} - 1)^2} \tag{3-109}$$

which is Einstein's heat capacity equation for a simple solid.

It is to be remembered that since these are independent harmonic oscillators vibrating about their individual points of equilibrium, it would not matter whether these equilibrium points were arranged on a crystal lattice of any structure whatsoever or whether the points were scattered in a disordered manner throughout space with no translation as in a "frozen" gravity-free gas. Consequently, 3–108 can be used with little alteration to compute the energy of vibration of a diatomic ideal gas. (This will be added to the translational energy and rotational energy later.)

In spite of the structureless aspects, Einstein's equation 3–109 gave results much in agreement with experiment. Debye improved this equation (in a manner we are not prepared to discuss at the moment) by considering that the vibrations of the atoms are coupled so that one can count the modes of motion rather than counting the atoms. To do this along the lines of the procedures of this text, we should consider a crystalline solid as a three-dimensional polyatomic molecule, and determine the normal coordinates before proceeding with the full treatment. This is avoided for the moment.

It is interesting and useful to anticipate that a person can prove that in a system which contains several kinds of energy such as rotational, translational, vibrational, electronic, etc.,

$$E = E_T + E_V + E_r + E_e + \cdots$$

has a multiplicative partition function

$$Q = Q_T Q_V Q_r Q_e \cdots$$

PROBLEMS

1. If dots were used twice as often as dashes in the Morse code, what would be the information I in a message of 1000 symbols?

2. If the double blank spaces between words were introduced as having meaning in the Morse code, and if the frequencies of occurrence were: dots $\frac{1}{3}$, dashes $\frac{1}{2}$, and double blank spaces $\frac{1}{6}$, what would be the information in 1000 such symbols?

3. (a) Picking out any seven letters of the alphabet, how many seven-letter combinations can you construct from the chosen letters (neglect the significance of meaning)?

(b) If all words that are the inverse of another word (like Natures and Serutan®) were ruled out, how much would the number of words in 3(a) be reduced?

4. (a) A decorator has a plaque 10 inches square which is to be covered with $\frac{3}{5}$ as many square black tiles $\frac{1}{2}$ in. square as white tiles $\frac{1}{2}$ in. square. Neglecting beauty and meaning or other considerations, how many designs can one make?

(b) What is the information I of the designs?

5. (a) A checkerboard having 32 black squares and 32 red squares fixed on it has 12 black and 12 red pieces movable on it. How many arrangements are there?

(b) If a line were drawn across the center of the checkerboard and antisymmetry were demanded, how would the problem be altered?

6. (a) Using Eq. 3–24 and the knowledge that $h = 6.62 \times 10^{-27}$ erg sec, and the mass of an electron is 9.11×10^{-28} grams, compute the allowed energy of an electron confined in a tube one centimeter long.

(b) If it were possible to measure the spectra from the electron in 6(a), what would be the wavelength of the first four lines?

7. A tuning fork has a ratio of restoring force constant to mass, $K/M = 8100$. What is the frequency of vibration?

8. (a) What energy is required to expand a mole of perfect gas at one atmosphere from $0°$ K to $1000°$?

(b) Compute the Helmholtz free energy of a perfect gas at $1000°K$ [beware of careless use of the answer to 8(a)].

9. Excerpts from a table furnished by Barnes, *et al.*, supplies the following data:

Compound	Atom Pair	m	m_2	μ	$K \times 10^{-5}$	Frequency Observed	Frequency Computed
1. C_2H_5	C—C	12	12	6	4.50	933	——
2. CH_3OH	C—O	12	16	6.85	5.77	1034	11.0
3. C_2H_4	C=C	12	12	6	9.77	1623	——
4. H_2CO	C=O	12	16	6.85	12.06	1744	1730
5. C_2H_2	C≡C	12	12	6	17.2	1975	——
6. CO	C≡O	12	16	6.85	5.07	2169	——
7. CH_4	C—H	12	1	0.92	5.08	2915	2920
8. HCN	C≡N	12	14	6.46	16.6	2089	——

The frequencies in this table are reported in reciprocal centimeters and must be multiplied by 3×10^{10} to get the frequency in cycles per second. The reduced mass is

$$\mu = \frac{m_1 m_2}{m_1 + m_2}$$

The frequencies are computed from the equation

$$\nu = \frac{1}{2\pi}\sqrt{\frac{K}{\mu}}$$

Complete the missing data in the last column of the table and compare the results with observation.

10. In the near infrared HCl has a vibrational band at a frequency of 8.65×10^{13} cycles per second. If you solve for the restoring force constant K, do you get 4.806×10^5 dynes per centimeter?

11. The Debye temperatures θ_D for some metals are given below:

Na	150°K	Ni	375
Cu	315	Pt	225
Zn	250	C (diamond)	1860

Knowing that the definition of the Debye temperature is

$$\theta_D = \frac{h\nu_D}{k}$$

Where k is Boltzmann's constant and h is Planck's constant, compute the Debye frequencies ν_D for these elements in the solid state.

NECESSARY
FOUNDATIONS
AND ILLUSTRATIVE
EXAMPLES

Introduction

The reader will notice upon studying this chapter that many parts of some rather complex problems can be solved without the use of quantum mechanics; this is so for such things as the entropy of mixing, but not for any problems in spectroscopy. But even when quanta can be ignored, the theory of probability is still with us in all problems. Also, the reader will notice that the first part of the chapter has to do with the philosophical connections between entropy and information theory.

It is justifiable to place great emphasis upon phase diagrams because in the author's opinion (which is shared by many others) equilibrium diagrams are a way of expressing some of the most basic findings of chemistry: solubility, phase changes, compound formation, precipitation, melting and boiling temperatures, eutectics, miscibility gaps, spinoidals and their role in nucleation, stoichiometry and many others.

4-1 The Purpose of this Chapter

The ultimate goal in the study of statistical mechanics is to be able to proceed freely with understanding and confidence in the solution of new problems as they come up. The investigator will find, however, that each individual problem has its own particular characteristics and it would be difficult to outline a clear-cut stepwise procedure that would apply to all cases. In this chapter, some of the simpler problems that have been worked out will be briefly described. These examples are not chosen because of their relative importance over all others that might have been chosen. Neither is the choice based on how recently the application was added to man's knowledge. The attempt is to give a range of examples that will touch upon many that the reader will encounter.

4-2 Statistical Mechanics and Thermodynamics

At this point we are going to go ahead of our physical understanding and present some results* for future use with the hope that their full meaning can be clarified later.

There are two ways by which the logarithm of the number of ways W of distributing atoms among the energy levels can be separated into two parts. The first way of doing this is as follows:

$$\ln W = \ln \frac{n!}{n_1! \, n_2! \, n_3! \cdots n_k!} = \ln \frac{n!}{\prod\limits_j^k n_j!}$$

$$= \ln n! - \sum_j \ln n_j! \tag{4-1}$$

Using the crudest of Stirling's approximations, i.e.,

$$\ln m! = m \ln m \tag{4-2}$$

we get Eq. 4-2 in the form

$$\ln W = n \ln n - \sum_j n_j \ln n_j \tag{4-3}$$

But since:

$$n_j = \frac{n}{Q} e^{-e_j/kT} \tag{4-4}$$

then

$$\ln W = n \ln n - \sum \frac{n}{Q} e^{-e_j/kT} \ln \frac{n}{Q} e^{-e_j/kT}$$

$$= n \ln n - \frac{n}{Q} \sum \left(e^{-e_j/kT} \ln \frac{n}{Q} + e^{-e_j/kT} \ln e^{-e_j/kT} \right) \tag{4-5}$$

$$= n \ln n - \frac{n}{Q} \left[\ln \frac{n}{Q} \sum e^{-e_j/kT} - \sum \frac{e_j}{kT} e^{-e_j/kT} \right]$$

Since

$$\sum e^{-e_j/kT} = Q$$

*Reference 25, pp. 235–236, and Ref. 10 in general.

then

$$\ln W = n \ln n - n \ln \frac{n}{Q} + \frac{1}{kT} \sum e_j e^{-e_j/kT} \tag{4-6}$$

Remember that

$$E = \sum_j e_j n_j = \sum e_j \frac{n}{Q} e^{-e_j/kT} = \frac{n}{Q} \sum e_j e^{-e_j/kT}$$

or

$$\sum e_j e^{-e_j/kT} = \frac{QE}{n}$$

Then Eq. 4-6 becomes

$$\ln W = n \ln n - n \ln \frac{n}{Q} + \frac{E}{kT} \tag{4-7}$$

One further step separates $n \ln n/Q$ into parts thus:

$$n \ln \frac{n}{Q} = n \ln n - n \ln Q$$

Then

$$\ln W = n \ln n - n \ln n + n \ln Q + \frac{E}{kT}$$

$$= n \ln Q + \frac{E}{kT} \tag{4-8}$$

Finally, multiplying through by kT, we convert the whole dimensionless Eq. 4-8 into energies

$$kT \ln W = nkT \ln Q + E \tag{4-9a}$$

or

$$E = -nkT \ln Q + kT \ln W \tag{4-9b}$$

In the above equation E is considered to be the total energy of the system as we can readily see, but what we wish to have the reader accept is the idea first that $-nkT \ln Q$ is the portion of the total energy E that is available for useful work or the Helmholtz free energy F:

$$F = -nkT \ln Q \tag{4-10}$$

and second that $Tk \ln W$ is the portion of E that is *not* available for any mechanical purposes such as one might get from a gas engine (or steam engine). The $k \ln W$ term, the useless energy expression, is called entropy S. Thereby Eq. 4-9(b) can be written

$$E = F + TS \tag{4-11}$$

This equation is usually seen as

$$F = E - TS \quad \text{or} \quad G = H - TS \tag{4-12}$$

and considered perhaps the most basic equation in the use of the second law of thermodynamics. In Eq. 4–12 G is the Gibbs free energy* and H is enthalpy.

$$H = E + PV$$

4-3 The Partition Function and A Priori Probability

At the beginning of this section, it was remarked that there are two ways of separating $\ln W$ into parts. The second way is as follows:

$$\ln W = -n \ln \sum_j p_j \ln p_j \tag{4-13}$$

where p_j is the a priori probability.

$$p_j = \frac{n_j}{n} = \frac{ne^{-e_j/kT}}{\sum ne^{-e_j/kT}} = \frac{e^{-e_j/kT}}{Q} \tag{4-14}$$

Then

$$\ln W = -n \sum \frac{e^{-e_j/kT}}{Q} \ln \left(\frac{e^{-e_j/kT}}{Q} \right) \tag{4-15}$$

$$= -\frac{n}{Q} \left(\sum e^{-e_j/kT} \ln e^{-e_j/kT} - \sum e^{-e_j/kT} \ln Q \right)$$

$$= \frac{n}{Q} \sum \frac{e_j}{kT} e^{-e_j/kT} + \frac{n}{Q} \ln Q \sum e^{-e_j/kT}$$

$$= \frac{E}{kT} + n \ln Q \tag{4-16a}$$

or

$$Tk \ln W = nk \, T \ln Q + E \tag{4-16b}$$

which checks with Eq. 4–9(a).

4-4 Summary Equations

There is a set of equations connecting the measurable quantities of original thermodynamics with those quantities which the statistical mechanists measure when armed with quantum mechanics and spectroscopy. The thermodynamic measurables are P, V, T, Q (the energy in the form of heat), and N (the amount of material often

*Different authors use different symbols for these terms; for example, some use F for the Gibbs free energy and A for Helmholtz free energy.

weighed and converted to moles). The statistical mechanic wants to use quantum mechanics to determine the partition function Q, and to keep the concepts of T, V, and N. This means that he has two fewer measurables, P and E. Both the thermodynamist and the statistical mechanic want to use their laboratory measurements to compute some ultimate quantities. They are F, S, C_v, for both, and in addition, for the statistical mechanist, P and E. The equations by which these quantities can be computed (making full use of the partition function Q) are, for localized systems,

(a) *Helmholtz free energy*

$$F = -kT \ln Q \qquad (4\text{-}17a)$$

(b) *Total energy*

$$E = kT^2 \left(\frac{\partial \ln Q}{\partial T} \right)_v = kT \left(\frac{d \ln Q}{d \ln T} \right)_v \qquad (4\text{-}17b)$$

(c) *Entropy*

$$S = -\left(\frac{\partial F}{\partial T} \right)_v = k \left[\ln Q - \left(\frac{\partial \ln Q}{\partial \ln T} \right)_v \right] \qquad (4\text{-}17c)$$

(d) *Pressure*

$$P = kT \left(\frac{\partial \ln Q}{\partial v} \right)_T \qquad (4\text{-}17d)$$

(e) *Heat capacity*

$$C_v = \left(\frac{\partial E}{\partial T} \right)_v = k \left[2 \left(\frac{\partial \ln Q}{\partial \ln T} \right)_v + T^2 \left(\frac{\partial^2 \ln Q}{\partial T^2} \right)_v \right] \qquad (4\text{-}17e)$$

In addition to these equations there is a set applicable to *enthalpy* H instead of E and *Gibbs* free energy G instead of F. The transformation can be made by knowing that

$$H = E + pv \qquad (4\text{-}18a)$$

(to account for ambient pressure) and

$$G = F + pv \qquad (4\text{-}18b)$$

so that

$$G = kT \left[-\ln Q + \left(\frac{\partial \ln Q}{\partial \ln v} \right)_T \right] \qquad (4\text{-}18c)$$

4-5 Nonlocalized Systems*

For nonlocalized systems, the various translating, vibrating, or rotating molecules share at large the same volume V, and the number of ways

*Reference 32, pp. 36–71, and Ref. 26, pp. 340–355.

W_n of arranging the N indistinguishable particles is less than that for localized systems by a factor $1/N!$, so that

$$W_{nL} = \frac{W_L}{N!} \quad \text{or} \quad \ln W_{nL} = \ln W_L - N \ln N \tag{4-19}$$

Taking $\ln W_L$ from Eq. 4–16a we have

$$\ln W_L = N \ln Q + \frac{E}{kT} \tag{4-20}$$

$$\ln W_{nL} = N \ln Q + \frac{E}{kT} - N \ln N$$

$$= N \ln \frac{Q}{N} - \frac{E}{kT}$$

Multiplying by kT gives

$$kT \ln W_{nL} = E + N \ln \frac{Q}{N} \tag{4-21}$$

Now we can drop the subscripts L and nL and, recognizing the parts of Eq. 4–21, write

$$TS = kT \ln W \tag{4-22}$$

and

$$F = -N \ln \frac{Q}{N} \tag{4-23}$$

The terms Q and E are unchanged. Rewriting Eqs. 4–17(a–c) for future reference for nonlocalized systems, we have

$$F = -NkT \ln \frac{Q}{N} \tag{4-24a}$$

$$E = kT^2 \left(\frac{\partial \ln Q}{\partial T}\right)_v = kT \left(\frac{d \ln Q}{d \ln T}\right)_v \tag{4-24b}$$

$$TS = NkT \ln \frac{Q}{N} + E \tag{4-24c}$$

4-6 Entropy and Information

In Sec. 3–5 we pointed out that information I could be thought about in two ways: (1) the logarithm of the number of ways of arranging the symbols expressed on the basis of log base 2 rather than base e or 10, and (2) the logarithm base e of the number of ways of arranging the symbols divided by the logarithm of 2 base e. Both ways of thinking give the same answer, but the second viewpoint is the more useful to us at this moment because it suggests that we measure

information in terms of units, i.e., bits, borrowed from the Morse code
which has $L = 2$, i.e., only two classes of events, a dot or a dash. The
reference system also has $p_1 = p_2 = \frac{1}{2}$, which means that it is a "flat"
system like our flat-rate theater. The information equation is

$$I = k \ln W \tag{4-25}$$

and the entropy equation is

$$S = k \ln W \tag{4-26}$$

but the k in the information equation is $k = 1/\ln 2$. Does the k in
the entropy equation have an analogous meaning?

We shall invent a "flat gas" and study its properties and see what
happens. We define a flat gas in almost the same way we defined a
perfect gas, except that it is in a different state. The flat gas has n
atoms each of mass m; the individual particle (or atom) occupies no
volume; and the particles do not attract one another or the walls of
the container. The difference between this gas and an ordinary perfect
gas is that the energies are not distributed; all atoms have exactly
the same energy per degree of freedom, that is, the average energy, $\bar{e}$.

$$e_j = \bar{e} = \frac{1}{2} kT = \frac{k}{2}(1°K) = \frac{k}{2} \tag{4-27}$$

We divide the gas into L equal compartments* with serial numbers
j on the compartments. The number in each compartment is

$$n_j = \frac{N}{L} \tag{4-28}$$

and the a priori probability for any one is

$$p_j = \frac{n_j}{N} = \frac{N}{L}\frac{1}{N} = \frac{1}{L} \tag{4-29}$$

$$\ln W_f = -N \sum p_j \ln p_j = -N \sum_1^L \frac{1}{L} \ln \frac{1}{L} = N \sum \frac{1}{L} \ln L$$

$$= N \ln L \tag{4-30}$$

(compare with Eq. 2-44(d)).

In this treatment of the flat gas everything depends upon how many
compartments L we divide the gas into. Let us take

$$L = e^{1/R} \tag{4-31}$$

where R is the gas constant. Then substituting Eq. 4-31 into Eq. 4-30,
we find

$$\ln W_f = N \ln e^{1/R} = \frac{N}{R} = \frac{1}{k} \tag{4-32}$$

*The term L here has the same meaning as does k in Eqs. 2-44(a-d).

Now going back to our statement regarding the second viewpoint of the information content, I_x, of any system X expressed in units of the Morse code

$$I_x = \frac{\ln W_x}{\ln W_2} = \frac{\ln W}{\ln 2} \tag{4-33}$$

We can now proceed to define our entropy S of any substance in units of the flat gas,

$$S = \frac{\ln W}{\ln W_f} = \frac{\ln W}{\dfrac{1}{k}} = k \ln W \tag{4-34}$$

The reader will find something absurd about dividing anything into L parts (where $L = e^{1/R}$) when he puts the actual value of R into the computations. This is related in part to the fact that the scale of temperature and Avogadro's number were devised independently at the beginning.

4-7 Some Remarks About Spectra

In view of the fact that all thermodynamic properties of a substance can be derived from the partition function, then it follows that these properties are ultimately dependent upon the measurable parameters that are in the partition function

$$Q = \sum_j \exp\left(\frac{-e_j}{kT}\right) = \sum \exp\left(\frac{-ef(j)}{kT}\right) \tag{4-35}$$

In the perfect gas, you remember, we found that

$$e = \frac{h^2}{8ma^2} \tag{4-36a}$$

and

$$f(j) = j^2$$

so

$$e_j = \frac{h^2 j^2}{8ma^2} \tag{4-36b}$$

whereas for the harmonic oscillator,

$$e = h\nu \tag{4-37a}$$

and

$$f(j) = (j + \tfrac{1}{2}) \quad \text{or} \quad (n + \tfrac{1}{2}) \tag{4-37b}$$

so

$$e_j = (n + \tfrac{1}{2})h\nu$$

When we were working with the Einstein solid, it was just assumed that the atoms vibrate harmonically about their equilibrium positions and using quantum theory we derived Eqs. 3–95 and 3–96. However, for materials that lend themselves to spectroscopy we have another source of data for computing the parameters in Q. Some illustrations of the use of spectra follow.

4-8 The Ideal Diatomic Gas, in Vibration

This gas is defined as an assemblage of diatomic molecules that do not attract one another, and the volume of the individual molecules themselves can be neglected in computing the volume of the container. In addition, the atoms within each molecule have an interacting force f upon each other that is linear.

$$f = m \frac{d^2(r - r_0)}{dt^2} = -K(r - r_0) \tag{4-38}$$

The potential energy is then

$$e(r) = \int f \, d(r - r_0) = -K \int (r - r_0) \, d(r - r_0)$$

$$= \epsilon - K(r - r_0)^2 \tag{4-39}$$

where e is the total energy. The frequency of vibration of this molecule is

$$\nu = \frac{1}{2\pi} \sqrt{\frac{K}{\mu}} \tag{4-40}$$

where

$$\mu = \frac{m_1 m_2}{m_1 + m_2} \quad \text{(the reduced mass)} \tag{4-41}$$

and m_1 and m_2 are the masses of the atoms in the molecules. This can be recognized as so many harmonic oscillators, much like those pertaining to an Einstein solid except that these oscillators are free to translate in a manner analogous to the perfect monotomic gas. The partition function then should be equal to the product of two partition functions: one being a partition function, Q_{tr} of translation and the other of vibration, Q_v.

$$Q = Q_{tr} Q_v = \left\{ \frac{[2\pi(m_1 + m_2)kT]^{3/2}}{h^3 N} \right\}^N \frac{e^{-((1/2)h\nu/kT)}}{1 - e^{-h\nu/kT}} \tag{4-42}$$

(see Eqs. 3–79 and 3–96).

Although no spectroscopic data are needed in determining Q_{tr}, the partition function of vibration cannot be determined without knowing either the frequency v or the constant from which it is derived (Eq. 3–88).

Figure 4–1 shows schematically a graph of $e(r)$ against $(r - r_0)$ as dictated by Eq. 4–39. But quantum theory does not permit all the continuous values of $e(r)$ that Fig. 4–1 suggests. The allowed values are

$$e(n) = (n + \tfrac{1}{2})hv \qquad\qquad (4\text{--}43)$$

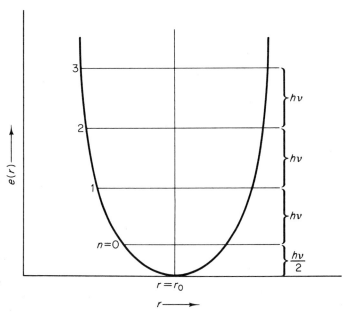

FIGURE 4-1   The energy diagram of a harmonic oscillator showing the equal spacing between the allowed energy levels.

A table of e_n against n is of interest. Table 4–1 shows the values of n and $(n + \tfrac{1}{2})$ in the first two columns, and in the third column $(n' + \tfrac{1}{2})$, where $n' = (n + 1)$. The last column gives the difference between $n' + \tfrac{1}{2}$ and $n + \tfrac{1}{2}$. Thus the spacing between the energy levels are all the same, i.e., hv. These equal spacings are shown in Fig. 4–1. When $n = 0$, the energy $e_0 = \tfrac{1}{2}hv$ is called the zero point energy.

Where spectroscopy comes in is in the determination of the frequency v_0. When the energy of vibration drops from $(n' + \tfrac{1}{2})hv$ to the level $(n + \tfrac{1}{2})hv$, radiation of frequency v is emitted and can be measured and introduced into Eq. 4–42.

Table 4–1

n	$n + \frac{1}{2}$	$n' + \frac{1}{2} = (n + 1) + \frac{1}{2}$	$[(n + 1) + \frac{1}{2}] - (n + \frac{1}{2})]$
0	$\frac{1}{2}$	$1\frac{1}{2}$	1
1	$1\frac{1}{2}$	$2\frac{1}{2}$	1
2	$2\frac{1}{2}$	$3\frac{1}{2}$	1
3	$3\frac{1}{2}$	$4\frac{1}{2}$	1
4	$4\frac{1}{2}$	$5\frac{1}{2}$	1
5	$5\frac{1}{2}$	$6\frac{1}{2}$	1
6	$6\frac{1}{2}$	$7\frac{1}{2}$	1

4-9 The Ideal Diatomic Gas in Rotation

The diatomic molecule exhibits discrete energy levels not only in vibration, but also in rotation. The result of solving the Schrödinger equation for the rotational energies of a diatomic molecule is

$$e_j = \frac{h^2 j(j + 1)}{8\pi^2 I} \equiv Bj(j + 1) \qquad (4\text{--}44)$$

where j is an integer, just as is n in Eq. 4–43. In Eq. 4–44, I is the moment of inertia (see Fig. 4–2).

$$I = \mu r^2 = \frac{m_1 m_2}{m_1 + m_2} r^2 \qquad (4\text{--}45)$$

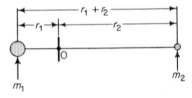

where r is the equilibrium distance between the atoms of masses m_1 and m_2. For this work it is assumed that r remains constant and the bond does not "stretch" as it does in vibration. Thus we are keeping the rotational and vibrational energies separate. For

FIGURE 4-2 The dumbbell molecule showing two atoms of unequal mass and their distances r_1 and r_2 from the center of gravity O. Here $r_1 + r_2 = r$ as used for computing the reduced mass μ.

more accurate computations "rotation-vibration" must be considered. We will not go into that here.*

When the rotating diatomic molecule drops from an energy level e'_j to e_j, there is an emission of radiation ν obeying equation

$$e'_j - e_j = h\nu \qquad (4\text{--}46)$$

so we expect that such jumps will emit radiation or absorb radiation (depending upon whether or not we use absorption spectra). Using

*See Ref. 18, p. 103.

Eq. 4–45, we get

$$\nu = \frac{B}{h}[j'(j'+1) - j(j+1)] \equiv \frac{B}{h}\Delta \qquad (4\text{–}47)$$

where $\Delta = [j'(j+1) - j(j+1)]$.

To know what values of j' and j are permissible we must know the selection rules. In rotational spectra $j' = j \pm 1$. Substituting $j' = (j+1)$ into Eq. 4–47, we find

$$\nu_j = \frac{2B}{h}(j+1) = \frac{B}{h}\Delta \qquad (4\text{–}48)$$

See Fig. 4–3 and compare with Fig. 4–1.

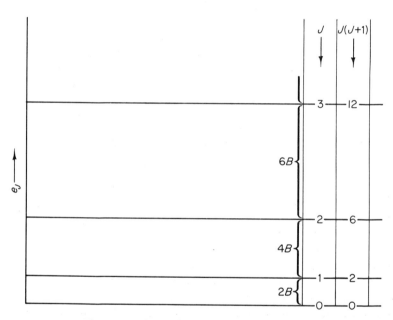

FIGURE **4-3** The energy levels for the rotating, rigid, diatomic molecule.

Now the reader might wonder why we need the spectral data when we do not use ν in Eq. 4–44. The answer is that we need to know I in Eq. 4–44 as defined by Eq. 4–45, in which we do not know r_0 (although we do know m_1 and m_2). So we use Eq. 4–46 to get B from the spectroscopically measured value of ν.

Now, knowing B and also being informed that the degeneracy of a rigid rotor is

$$\omega_j = (2j+1) \qquad (4\text{–}49)$$

we can evaluate the partition function of rotation

$$Q_r = \sum_j \omega_j e^{-e_j/kT}$$

$$= \sum_j (2j + 1)e^{-Bj(j+1)/kT}$$

$$= N(1 + 3e^{-2B/kT} + 5e^{-6B/kT} + 7e^{-12B/kT} + \cdots) \qquad (4\text{-}50)$$

When the difference between energy levels is small compared to kT, then Eq. 4–50 can be approximated by integration.

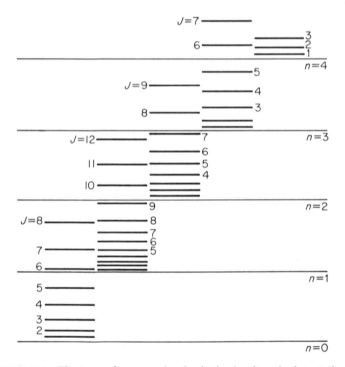

FIGURE **4-4** The type of energy level obtained when both rotation and vibration are involved.

$$Q_r = N \int (2j + 1)e^{-Bj(j+1)/kT} \, dj$$

$$= N \frac{8\pi^2 IkT}{h^2} = \frac{NkT}{B} \qquad (4\text{-}51)$$

When $m_1 = m_2$, then we have a thing called *symmetry number*, usually given the symbol σ. In this case it is two, since there are two indistinguishable ways of placing a molecule of this symmetry. For molecules such as H_2, N_2, and Cl_2 (as contrasted to CO and HCl), all have

$$Q_r = \frac{N8\pi^2 IkT}{\sigma h^2} = \frac{NkT}{\sigma B} \qquad (4\text{-}52)$$

4-10   Characteristic Temperature

It is stylish among some workers to define a new term called "characteristic temperature." For rotation it is θ_r

$$\theta_r = \frac{h^2}{8\pi Ik} \qquad (4\text{-}53)$$

and Eq. 4–52 becomes

$$Q_r = \frac{NT}{\sigma Q_r} \qquad (4\text{-}54)$$

The characteristic temperature for vibration is

$$\theta_v = \frac{h\nu}{k} \qquad (4\text{-}55)$$

and Eq. 4–35 becomes

$$Q_v = \frac{e^{-\theta_v/2T}}{1 - e^{-\theta_v/T}} \qquad (4\text{-}56)$$

In addition to the translation, vibration, and rotation terms there is also an electronic partition function Q_e. So the extended and comprehensive form of Eq. 4–42 is

$$Q = Q_{tr} Q_v Q_r Q_e$$
$$= \left[\frac{2\pi(m_1 + m_2)(kT)^{3/2}}{h^3 N} \right]^N \left(\frac{e^{-((1/2)h\nu/kT)}}{1 - e^{-h\nu/kT}} \right)^{3N} \left(\frac{8\pi^2 IkT}{h^2} \right)^N Q_e \qquad (4\text{-}57)$$

The electronic levels will not be discussed here except to refer to Fig. 4–6 and say that when an atom or pair of atoms have their electrons raised to a higher level, this energy is added to the other energies such as translation and rotation and obeys the distribution laws such as

$$n_j = \frac{Ne^{-e_j/kT}}{Q} \qquad (4\text{-}58)$$

This equation incorporates all manner of energies e_j that can exist.

4-11   The Practical Diatomic Gas Molecule*

Most diatomic molecules do not exhibit a linear restoring force of attraction between the atoms as expressed in Eq. 3–81 with a parabolic

*Reference 18, pp. 98–102, and Ref. 26, pp. 404–409.

energy function as shown in Eq. 3–81 and Fig. 4–1. The potential energy is very nearly equivalent to the Morse function, according to

$$e(r) = e_0(1 - e^{-\beta(r-r_0)})^2 \qquad (4\text{–}59)$$

and Fig. 4–5. In this equation e_0 is the energy of dissociation of the molecule, i.e., the energy required to separate the atoms an infinite distance apart. For small displacements from r_0 the curve fits closely to the parabola shown in dotted lines in Fig. 4–5. Thus at low tem-

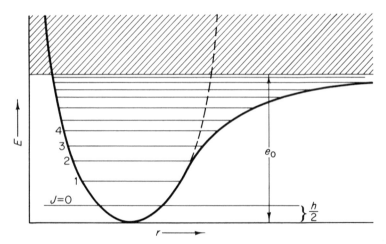

FIGURE 4-5 The Morse curve showing the crowding of the energy levels at the top.

peratures one can get fairly satisfactory results using the linear restoring force theory. At high energies the Morse curve is necessary. Such an energy curve as is expressed in Eq. 4–59 has been subjected to the Schrödinger treatment, yielding

$$e_j = h\nu_e\left(j + \frac{1}{2}\right) - \left(\frac{h\nu_e}{4D}\right)^2\left(j + \frac{1}{2}\right)^2 \qquad (4\text{–}60\text{a})$$

and by older classical methods

$$e_j = h\nu_e(j + \tfrac{1}{2}) - Xh\nu_e(j + \tfrac{1}{2})^2 \qquad (4\text{–}60\text{b})$$

In Eq. 4–60a the term D is a necessary constant, and in Eq. 4–60b the term X is an empirical constant called the anharmonicity factor.

As may be seen from Eq. 4–60a, the energy levels are not equally spaced. As shown in Fig. 4–5, they get crowded together at the top as $e_j \rightarrow e_0$ and should theoretically have the same spacings that are found in a perfect gas in translation.

When these molecules have their atoms electronically excited, there are curves for each excited state, as shown in Fig. 4–6. For the reader who likes to think of theaters, we have a theater in which there is a complicated scale of charges for the sections on the main floor as shown in Eq. 4–60a, and then there are as many balconies as there are electronic states, each with its own scale. Polyatomic molecules will not be dwelt upon here, but we refer the reader to Refs. 18 and 36.

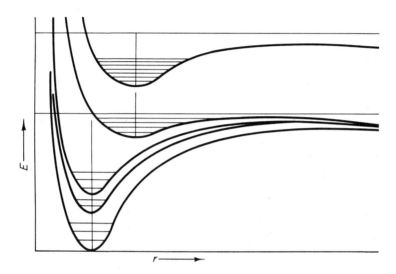

FIGURE **4-6** Morse curves for various electronic states of excitation.

4-12 Continuous Solid Solutions*

Besides the many equilibrium problems that have been solved solely with thermodynamics, there are others which can be solved without the use of quantum mechanics. An example of a problem dealing with statistical mechanics without quantum mechanics is the problem of solutions of metals in one another in the solid state. These solutions can easily come about when two metals A and B have the same crystal structure and the atoms of A and B have nearly the same radius. This means that some of the atoms of B can go to the lattice sites of A and remain there without distorting the structure of A very much. Figure 4–7† shows an almost perfect example of this sort of thing in

*In preparation for the remainder of this chapter, see Ref. 20, pp. 271–327, Ref. 12, pp. 127–150, Ref. 7, Chaps. 12 and 13, Ref. 16, Chap. 7, and Ref. 32, pp, 270–290.
†Figures 4–7, 4–8, 4–11(a–b), 4–12, 4–13, 4–14, 4–15, 4–16, and 4–17 are redrawn from Ref. 17.

the case of alloys of silver and gold. Both of these metals, in the pure state, crystallize as face-centered cubic, and the coordination number (or the number of nearest neighbors) is $W = 12$. Their atomic radii are almost identical: 1.44 angstrom units $= 1.44 \times 10^{-8}$ cm. Their heats of sublimation are 68,400 calories per mole for Ag and 84,700 for Au,

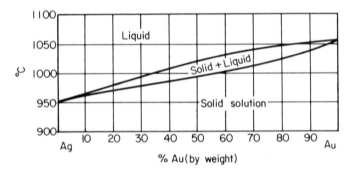

FIGURE **4-7** The almost ideal solid solution of silver and gold.

showing that the energy of attraction for like atoms is greater for gold than for silver, and the temperatures of melting of the pure substances are correspondingly different, 961°C for Ag and 1063°C for Au. Figure 4–8 shows a less ideal case.

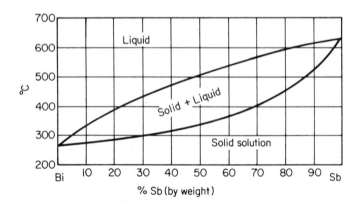

FIGURE **4-8** A less ideal example of solubility illustrated by bismuth and antimony.

Aside from these almost ideal solutions, there are examples of islands of insolubility sometimes far below the melting curves, as are shown in Fig. 4–9. We shall discuss first these insolubility gaps as shown in Fig. 4–9 and wait until Sec. 4–17 to discuss curves as shown in Figs. 4–7 and 4–8.

Let us consider a general case as follows: We have an alloy of *A* atoms and *B* atoms which can substitute for each other in the lattice

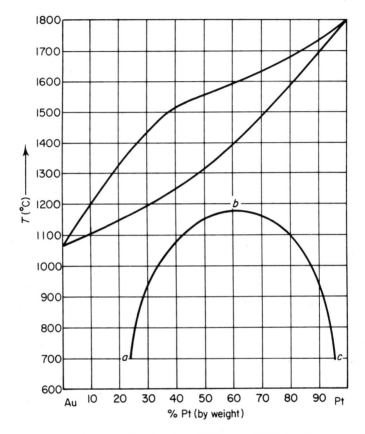

FIGURE 4-9 An example of a "miscibility gap." Under the curve *abc*, the gold and platinum atoms do not occupy lattice sites in the same crystal, but two separate kinds of crystals form; one kind is of gold and the other platinum. This happens when the energies of attraction for like atoms E_{aa} and E_{bb} are greater in magnitude than that for the unlike atoms E_{ab} (see Eq. 4–67).

sites. Let us choose an arbitrary composition consisting of N_A *A* atoms and N_B *B* atoms so that the fraction of *A* atoms is

$$f = \frac{N_A}{N} \qquad (4\text{–}61)$$

and the fraction of B atoms is

$$(1 - f) = \frac{N_B}{N} \tag{4-62}$$

where N is the total number of atoms. Let us pick any site out of the N sites and say that the chance that this site contains an A atom is $f = N_A/N$. The chance that a second atom next to the first A atom is also an A atom is, again, f. But since there are W nearest atoms, the chance that an A atom has a nearest neighbor that is also an A atom is

$$C_{A-A} = C_A(WC_A) = WC_A^2 = Wf^2 \tag{4-63}$$

The total number of A–A bonds in the structure is

$$N_{A-A} = \frac{NWf^2}{2} \tag{4-64}$$

The denominator 2 is introduced to keep from counting all the bonds twice. By the same line of reasoning, we conclude that the number of B–B bonds is

$$N_{B-B} = \frac{NW(1 - f)^2}{2} \tag{4-65}$$

and the number of A–B bonds is

$$N_{A-B} = NWf(1 - f) \tag{4-66}$$

Letting the energies of the types of bonds be E_{AA}, E_{BB}, and E_{A-B}, then the total energy of the system of bonds at this composition is

$$E = N_{A-A}E_{AA} + N_{BB}E_{BB} + N_{AB}E_{AB}$$
$$= \frac{NW}{2}[E_{AA}f^2 + E_{BB}(1 - f)^2 + 2E_{AB}f(1 - f)] \tag{4-67}$$

To get the change in energy during the mixing (or the formation of the alloy), we must subtract the energy of the pure metals before mixing:

$$E_0 = N_{AA}WE_{AA} + N_{BB}WE_{BB}$$
$$= \frac{NW}{2}[fE_{AA} + (1 - f)E_{BB}] \tag{4-68}$$

Subtracting the last two equations gives us the change in energy on mixing.

$$\Delta E = E - E_0 = \frac{NW}{2}f(1 - f)(2E_{AB} - E_{AA} - E_{BB}] \tag{4-69}$$

Before we go further, it is of interest that Eq. 4-69 shows that if the energy of attraction between unlike atoms were the arithmetical mean

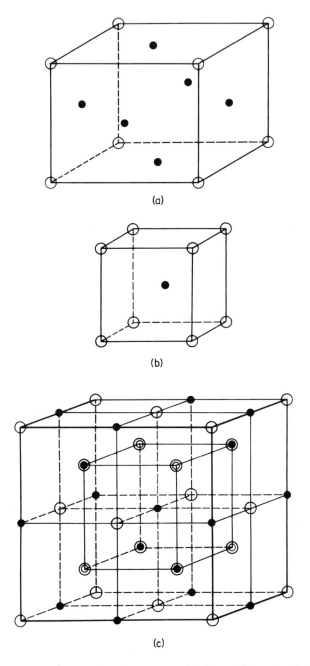

FIGURE **4-10** Some ordered structures. (a) One of the ordered structures of copper-gold (Cu_3Au). (b) The ordered structure of β-brass (CuZn). (c) The four kinds of lattice sites possible in the iron-aluminum system.

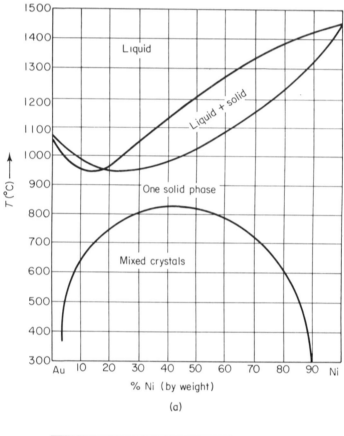

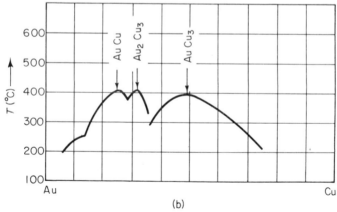

FIGURE **4-11** (a) The gap in the gold-nickel system. (b) The three preferred compositions for the ordered states in the gold-copper system. [See Fig. 4–10(a) for the AuCu₃ ordered structure.]

$$\Omega = \frac{r-w}{N} = \frac{r-w}{r+w} = \frac{N-2w}{N} \qquad (4\text{--}77)$$

so Ω is a fraction representing the ratio of difference between the number of right and wrong sites and the total sites. When no atoms are in the wrong position, $w = 0$ and $\Omega = 1$, i.e., complete order. Also, when all atoms are in the wrong positions then $r = 0$ and $\Omega = -1$, which is just as orderly as its counterpart. When the atoms are 50 per cent wrong and 50 per cent right, then $r = w$, and $\Omega = 0$, i.e., complete disorder.

Neglecting thermal entropy or electronic entropy, we can consider only the entropy of configuration as we did before.*

$$S = k \ln W = k \ln \frac{N!}{r!w!} \doteq k \ln \frac{N^N}{r^r w^w} \qquad (4\text{--}78)$$

$$= k(N \ln N - r \ln r - w \ln w) \qquad (4\text{--}79)$$

Letting

$$r = fN \quad \text{and} \quad w = (1-f)N \qquad (4\text{--}80)$$

where f is the fraction of sites that are right, we have

$$S = k[N \ln N - Nf \ln Nf - N(1-f) \ln N(1-f)]$$
$$= kN[\ln N - f \ln N - f \ln f - (1-f) \ln N - (1-f) \ln (1-f)]$$
$$= kN[\ln N - f \ln N - (1-f) \ln N - f \ln f - (1-f) \ln (1-f)]$$
$$= -kN[f \ln f + (1-f) \ln (1-f)] \qquad (4\text{--}81)$$

But this substitution changes our terminology in the definition of order in Eq. 4–77. Now Ω is

$$\Omega = \frac{r-w}{N} = \frac{Nf - N(1-f)}{N} = 2f - 1 \qquad (4\text{--}82)$$

which is even more convenient than before. The entropy from the disordering process† is

$$\Delta S = S - S_0 = -kN[f \ln f + (1-f) \ln (1-f)] \qquad (4\text{--}83)$$

The reader will see that this is the same as Eq. 4–73, but we must keep in mind that f in Eq. 4–73 referred to fractional composition, whereas Eq. 4–81 assumes a constant composition of $\frac{1}{2}$ in the case of Cu-Zn [see Fig. 4–10(b)] with f as the fraction of right sites. And by almost the same line of reasoning that was used before, one gets the energy in changing order to be

*We hope that the reader will not confuse the two W's used in this equation, where one W means "ways" and the other "coordination mumber."

†Notice that when $f = 1$ is substituted into Eq. (4–80) the entropy of the ordered state becomes zero.

$$\Delta E = -f(1 - f)\frac{NW}{2}[2E_{AB} - E_{AA} - E_{BB}] \qquad (4\text{-}84)$$

where W is the coordination number (compare with Eq. 4-69, but beware of the meaning of f). When applied to Cu-Zn, W in Eq. 4-84 is 8. Combining Eqs. 4-80 and 4-84, we have

$$\Delta F = \Delta E - T\,\Delta S = -f(1 - f)\frac{NW}{2}[2E_{AB} - E_{AA} - E_{BB}]$$

$$+ NkT[f \ln f + (1 - f) \ln (1 - f)]$$

$$= \frac{N}{2}\{Lf(1 - f) + 2kT[f \ln f + (1 - f) \ln (1 - f)]\} \qquad (4\text{-}85)$$

where, as before, $L = W[2E_{AB} - E_{AA} - E_{BB}]$. To find the minimum ΔF we differentiate and equate to zero, getting

$$\frac{L}{2}(1 - 2f) + kT \ln \frac{f}{1 - f} = 0 \qquad (4\text{-}86)$$

(compare with Eq. 4-75). Then

$$\frac{f}{1 - f} = e^{-L(1-2f)/2kT} \qquad (4\text{-}87)$$

Since $\Omega = 2f - 1$ (Eq. 4-82), this equation becomes

$$\frac{f}{1 - f} = e^{L\Omega/2kT} \qquad (4\text{-}88)$$

In the original Bragg and Williams work, it was assumed that the energy to cause disorder was

$$\phi = \phi_0 \Omega \qquad (4\text{-}89)$$

and that

$$\phi_0 = \frac{W}{2}[2E_{AB} - E_{AA} - E_{BB}]$$

which corresponds in our terminology to

$$\phi_0 = L \quad \text{and} \quad \phi = L\Omega \qquad (4\text{-}90)$$

So Eq. 4-88 becomes

$$\frac{f}{1 - f} = e^{\phi_0 \Omega/2kT} \qquad (4\text{-}91)$$

Or in terms of Ω throughout (letting $f = (1 + \Omega)/2$ from Eq. 4-82), we have

$$\Omega = [(1 - \Omega)e^{\phi_0 \Omega/2kT} - 1] \qquad (4\text{-}92)$$

which Bragg and Williams showed to be equivalent to the equation

$$\Omega = \tan h\left(\frac{\phi_0 \Omega}{4kT}\right) \qquad (4\text{-}93)$$

When Eq. 4–92 or 4–93 is used to plot Ω against T, Ω becomes zero at a temperature designated T_c, called the critical temperature, higher than which complete disorder prevails. To do this plot, it is easier to solve for T in Eq. 4–92 and substitute in various values of Ω. To get the value of T_c analytically, it is convenient to differentiate the free energy equation 4–85 twice with respect to f and equate to zero. The results of such a differentiation are called the spinoidal (or inflection points) of the ΔF curve. And the value of T_c is

$$T_c = \frac{L}{4k} \tag{4-94}$$

We want to give a hint here to the reader regarding Eq. (4–93). Although Bragg and Williams used series methods to get the hyperbolic tangent equation, there is a more direct way. If we apply the two equations (see Eqs. 4–77, 4–80, and 4–91),

$$\frac{r - W}{r + W} = \Omega$$

and

$$\frac{w}{r} = e^{-\phi_0\Omega/2kT} \tag{4-95}$$

to the elimination of w we get

$$\Omega = \frac{r - re^{-\phi_0\Omega/2kT}}{r + re^{-\phi_0\Omega/2kT}} = \frac{1 - e^{-\phi_0\Omega/2kT}}{1 + e^{-\phi_0\Omega/2kT}} \equiv \frac{1 - e^{-X}}{1 + e^{-X}} \tag{4-96}$$

where X replaces $\phi_0\Omega/2kT$.

Multiplying top and bottom by $e^{X/2}$,

$$\Omega = \frac{e^{X/2}(1 - e^{-X})}{e^{X/2}(1 + e^{-X})} = \frac{e^{X/2} - e^{-X}e^{X/2}}{e^{X/2} + e^{-X}e^{X/2}} = \frac{e^{X/2} - e^{-X/2}}{e^{X/2} + e^{-X/2}} \tag{4-97}$$

The last term is the definition of the hyperbolic tangent; therefore,

$$\Omega = \frac{e^{X/2} - e^{-X/2}}{e^{X/2} + e^{-X/2}} = \tanh \frac{X}{2} = \tan \frac{\phi_0\Omega}{4kT} \tag{4-98}$$

in agreement with Eq. 4–93.

4-14   Vacancies in Metals*

A subject which has similarities with the two previous subjects (solid solutions and order-disorder) is that of vacancies in metals. The results of this work have led to a thought that does not come naturally to the everyday crystallographer. That is, the thought that a *perfect* crystal

*See, for example, A. J. Dekker, *Solid State Physics* (Englewood Cliffs, N. J.: Prentice-Hall, Inc., 1961), pp. 62–67.

at room temperature cannot exist for the simple reason that it "doesn't want to." It is thermodynamically easier for a crystal to have some vacant lattice sites than to have them all filled. The general tendencies which oppose one another [(1) the tendency of atoms to fall to positions of lowest potential energy and thus become ordered and (2) the tendency of atoms to be arranged in that configuration for which there is the largest possible number of ways of attaining that configuration (or distribution)] result in a compromise wherein the tendencies are equally influential. The first of these tendencies would make E a minimum, and the second would make S a maximum. The resulting influences cause the Helmholtz free energy F to attain a minimum value according to

$$\Delta F = \Delta E - T\,\Delta S$$

Suppose that a crystal has $N + n$ lattice sites where atoms might be located, but that N of these sites are occupied and n of the sites are vacant. The number of ways that the vacancies can be distributed through the crystal is

$$W = \frac{(N+n)!}{N!\,n!} \tag{4-99}$$

Since the entropy $S_0 = 0$ when $n = 0$, then

$$\Delta S = k \ln W = k[(N+n)\ln(N+n) - N \ln N - n \ln n] \tag{4-100}$$

If the energy required to produce a vacancy is $\mathscr{E}$, then

$$\Delta E = n\mathscr{E} \tag{4-101}$$

and

$$\frac{\partial F}{\partial n} = \mathscr{E} - Tk\left[\frac{N}{N+n} + \frac{n}{N+n} + \ln(N+n) - \frac{n}{n} - \ln n\right]$$

$$= \mathscr{E} - Tk\left(\ln \frac{N+n}{n}\right) = 0 \tag{4-102}$$

or

$$\frac{n}{N+n} = e^{-\mathscr{E}/kT} \tag{4-103}$$

For small values of n as are encountered at temperatures sufficiently below the melting point of a metal, $(N + n)$ differs little from N, and Eq. 4-103 becomes

$$n = Ne^{-\mathscr{E}/kT} \tag{4-104}$$

Equation 4-104 shows that the number of vacancies increases with increasing temperature. If one were justified in assuming that the

energy required to produce a mole of vacancies is about one-fifth*
the energy required to vaporize a mole of metal, say 134,800/5 calories for Pt and 81,100/5 for Cu, then, according to Eq. 4–104,

$$\frac{n}{N}\,(\text{Pt, } 100°\text{K}) = e^{-134,800/(5 \times 2 \times 100)} = 10^{-58.5}$$

$$\frac{n}{N}\,(\text{Cu, } 100°\text{K}) = e^{-81,000/(2.3 \times 5 \times 2 \times 100)} = 10^{-35.0}$$

At $1000°\text{K}$, n/N for Pt would be about 10^{-6} and for Cu about $10^{-3.5}$.
These ratios are small, but the actual number of individual vacancies
per mole of Pt at $1000°\text{K}$ is $n/N \times N = n/N \times 6.02 \times 10^{23} \doteq 10^{17}$ and
for Cu, about $10^{19.5}$. These vacancies are important in, for example,
Eyring's theories of viscosity and in all theories of diffusion.

Some consideration has been given to another contribution to the
entropy change during the formation of vacancies, that is, the thermal
contribution. This has been presented by Dekker† briefly as follows.
In a crystal without vacancies each atom is equivalent to a harmonic
oscillator having three degrees of freedom as postulated in the Einstein
model of a solid. The frequency of vibration is ν. If W is the coordination number of the atom at a lattice site, then about each vacancy
there are W atoms that are not as firmly restored to their equilibrium
positions as are the atoms at the fully surrounded sites. The frequencies of these atoms neighboring a vacancy are consequently lower.
Call this vacancy ν'. Thus there are

$$3nW \text{ oscillators of frequency } \nu'$$

and

$$3(N - nW) \text{ oscillators of frequency } \nu$$

To compute the entropy due to thermal energy, we must first determine the number of ways that the energy can be distributed between
$3N$ harmonic oscillators without vacancies. But the energy comes in
packets of $h\nu$ each and the energy is $3nh\nu$. So the problem is that of
finding the number of ways W of distributing n packets of energy on
N lattice sites.

$$W = \frac{(N + n)!}{N!\,n!} \tag{4–105}$$

$$S_{\text{th}} = k[(N + n) \ln (N + n) - N \ln N - n \ln n]$$

$$= k\left[(N + n) \ln (N + n) + N \ln \frac{1}{N} - n \ln n - N \ln n + N \ln n\right]$$

*From experimental work.
†A. J. Dekker, *Solid State Physics* (Englewood Cliffs, N. J.: Prentice-Hall, Inc.,
1961).

$$= k\left[(N + n) \ln (N + n) + N \ln \frac{n}{N} - (N + n) \ln n\right]$$

$$= kN\left[\left(1 + \frac{n}{N}\right) \ln \left(1 + \frac{N}{n}\right) + \ln \frac{n}{N}\right] \tag{4-106}$$

This is analogous to

$$kN\left[\left(1 + \frac{1}{x}\right) \ln (1 + x) + B\right]$$

But according to L'Hospital's rule we have:

The limit of $\left(1 + \dfrac{1}{x}\right) \ln (1 + x)$ as x approaches zero is unity.

So Eq. 4–105 becomes

$$S_{\text{th}} = Nk\left[1 + \ln \frac{n}{N}\right]$$

Now if

$$nh\nu = NkT$$

then

$$\frac{n}{N} = \frac{kT}{h\nu}$$

and

$$S_{\text{th}} = Nk\left(1 + \ln \frac{kT}{h\nu}\right) \tag{4-107}$$

for the thermal entropy of a crystal (approximately when $h\nu$ is small compared to kT) without vacancies.

Analogously, going back to the crystal with $3nW$ oscillators of frequency ν' and $3(N - nW)$ oscillators of frequency ν, we can say that the thermal entropy is

$$S_{\text{th}} = k\left[3Wn\left(1 + \ln \frac{kT}{h\nu'}\right) + 3W(N - n)\left(1 + \ln \frac{kT}{h\nu}\right)\right] \tag{4-108}$$

Subtracting Eq. 4–107 from Eq. 4–108 gives

$$\Delta S_{\text{th}} = 3Wk \ln \frac{\nu}{\nu'} \tag{4-109}$$

per vacancy.

Adding the thermal entropy change of Eq. 4–109 to the configurational entropy change of Eq. 4–100 and duly processing, then instead of Eq. 4–104 we get

$$n = N\left(\frac{\nu}{\nu'}\right)^{3W} e^{-\mathcal{E}/kT} \tag{4-110}$$

Of course, Eq. 4-110 predicts a number of vacancies greater than that of Eq. 4-104 by a factor of $(v/v')^{3W}$ which for a close-packed crystal is a factor of $(v/v')^{3 \times 12} = (v/v')^{36}$ and if v were as much as five per cent greater than v', this could be important.

$$(1.05)^{36} = 5.79 \text{ fold}$$

However, these equations only apply when n is small compared to N. We know that as n increases, the probability of an atom's having two or more vacant adjacent sites increases; this not only makes v' a function of n, but it also reduces the energy E required to make further vacancies. One might expect the energy required for making vacancies to be reduced from one fifth the heat of sublimation (at room temperatures) to one twentieth of the heat of sublimation (at the melting point).

4-15 Equilibrium Between the Condensed Phase and the Vapor Phase

In the last three sections we discussed (1) equilibrium between a dissolved phase of two components and separated phases, (2) equilibrium between the ordered and disordered states of a solid, and (3) the equilibrium number of vacancies in a solid above 0°K. These all deal with solids, whereas this section deals with equilibrium between solid and vapor (or gas) and the section following this one is to deal with equilibrium between solid and liquid.

The subject of equilibrium between solid and its vapor* is really a matter of computing the vapor pressure of a condensed phase whose partition function is known. However, it has been found more convenient by most authors to ignore the partition function of the condensed phase and to determine the pressure from the entropy change on vaporization.

We have previously shown that

$$S_V = k \ln Q + \frac{E}{T} \tag{4-111}$$

For a perfect monatomic gas we must use the nonlocalized partition function Q'.

$$Q' = \frac{Q^N}{N!} = \left[\left(\frac{2\pi mkT}{h^2} \right)^{3/2} \right]^N \frac{1}{N!} \tag{4-112}$$

*A good discussion of vapor pressure is given in Ref. 26, pp. 309-313 and 355-359.

$$S_V = k \ln \left[\left(\frac{2\pi mkT}{h^2} \right)^{3/2} V \right]^N \frac{1}{N!} + \frac{E}{T}$$

$$= Nk \left\{ \ln \left[\left(\frac{2\pi mkT}{h^2} \right)^{3/2} V \right] - \frac{1}{N} \ln N! \right\} + \frac{E}{T} \qquad (4\text{-}113)$$

Using Stirling's second approximation [see Eq. 1–29(b)] and the facts that E for a perfect gas is $\frac{3}{2} NkT$ and $V = NkT/P$, we have

$$S_V = Nk \left\{ \ln \left[\left(\frac{2\pi mkT}{h^2} \right)^{3/2} \frac{NkT}{P} \right] - \frac{N \ln N + N}{N} \right\} + \frac{3}{2} Nk$$

$$= Nk \left[\ln \left(\frac{2\pi mkT}{h^2} \right)^{3/2} + \ln NkT - \ln P - \ln N + 1 + \frac{3}{2} \right]$$

$$= Nk \left[\ln \left(\frac{2\pi mkT}{h^2} \right)^{3/2} kT - \ln P + \frac{5}{2} \right] \qquad (4\text{-}114)$$

We know that the increase in entropy on vaporization is

$$\Delta S = \frac{\lambda(T)}{T} \qquad (4\text{-}115)$$

where $\lambda(T)$ is the heat of vaporization or sublimation at the temperature T. This is not independent of temperature, and this fact must be taken into consideration later. So the entropy of the atoms changes by an amount $\lambda(T)/T$ upon vaporization.

$$S_V = S_S + \frac{\lambda(T)}{T} \qquad (4\text{-}116)$$

where S_s is the entropy of the solid, which also varies with temperature according to

$$S_S = S_0 + \int_0^T \frac{C_p}{T} dT \qquad (4\text{-}117)$$

where S_0 is the entropy at $0°$K. By the third law of thermodynamics, $S_0 = 0$ for a solid. Substituting Eq. 4–117 into Eq. 4–116 gives

$$S_V = \frac{\lambda(T)}{T} + \int_0^T C_{pS} \frac{dT}{T} \qquad (4\text{-}118)$$

Now equating Eqs. 4–118 and 4–114, we have

$$\frac{\lambda(T)}{T} + \int_0^T C_{pS} d\ln T = Nk \left[\ln \left(\frac{2\pi mkT}{h^2} \right)^{3/2} kT - \ln P + \frac{5}{2} \right] \qquad (4\text{-}119)$$

$$\ln P = -\frac{\lambda(T)}{NkT} - \int_0^T C_{pS} d\ln T + \ln \left(\frac{2\pi mkT}{h^2} \right)^{3/2} kT + \frac{5}{2} \qquad (4\text{-}120)$$

To take care of the variation of heat of vaporization with temperature we use a statement from Kirchhoff which says that the heat of vaporization at any temperature is equal to the heat at absolute zero λ_0

plus the integral over the temperature of the differences in the heat capacities of the condensed and vapor phases.

$$\lambda(T) = \lambda_0 + \int_0^T C_{pV} - C_{pS})\, dT \tag{4-121}$$

But since $C_{pV} = \frac{5}{2} R$, Eq. 4-121 becomes

$$\lambda(T) = \lambda_0 + \frac{5}{2} NkT - \int_0^T C_{pS}\, dT \tag{4-122}$$

Substituting 4-122 into 4-120 gives*

$$\ln P = -\frac{\lambda_0}{RT} + \frac{5}{2}\ln T + \frac{1}{RT}\int_0^T C_{pS}\, dT + \frac{1}{R}\int_0^T C_{pS}\, d\ln T$$

$$+ \ln\left(\frac{2\pi mkT}{h^2}\right)^{3/2} \tag{4-123}$$

The last term in Eq. 4-123 was recognized long before the quantum and statistical mechanics were developed for it and was called the "vapor pressure constant" (or Sakur-Tetrode constant) and was merely designated by a letter i or j, or such. Also, Eq. 4-123 is not wholly a theoretical equation, because unlike C_v (heat capacity at constant volume which can be computed theoretically from such equations as 3-109), the term C_p cannot as yet be satisfactorily derived, and our values depend upon cryogenic experiments. Also λ_0 is a strictly experimental term.

For convenience Eq. 4-123 can be written

$$\ln P = -\frac{\lambda_0}{RT} + \mathscr{R} \quad \text{or} \quad P = e^{-(\lambda_0/RT) - \mathscr{R}} \tag{4-124}$$

where the $\mathscr{R}$ term is the remainder of $\ln p$ beyond λ_0/RT. The term that varies the most in Eq. 4-123 as we go from one simple structural type of a crystal to another is the heat of sublimation λ_0. If two crystals have nearly the same structures the C_p terms might be very nearly the same. Comparing two crystals, we have

$$P_2 = e^{\mathscr{R}} e^{-\lambda_{02}/RT}$$
$$P_1 = e^{\mathscr{R}} e^{-\lambda_{01}/RT} \tag{4-125}$$

Therefore,

$$P_2 = P_1 e^{-(\lambda_{02} - \lambda_{01})/RT}$$

Also, over a short temperature range a single substance can be vaporized or sublimed, and according to Eq. 4-124 a graph of $\ln P$ against $1/T$ gives an almost straight line whose slope (which is negative) gives the heat of sublimation in that temperature range.

*This conclusion is called the Sakur-Tetrode equation.

4-16 Equilibrium Between Reactive Molecules*

When two or more molecules or ions react to produce other molecules, an equilibrium concentration of the reactants and products is finally reached and after that no further change in concentration takes place. At this time the reaction is said to be complete. The concentrations at equilibrium can be used to compute the "equilibrium constant" K and the law of mass action can be considered and correlated mathematically with the free energy.

Such computations as we are considering are most easily handled when we do not have to worry about the molecules, ions, or atoms being too close together. This ease of handling is attained when (1) the reactants and products are in a dilute gaseous state, that is, when the gas is not under very great pressure or is diluted with an inert gas such as helium, or (2) when the reactants and products are soluble in some liquid solvent which does not enter the reaction. Consequently, our studies will be confined to gaseous reactions and reactions in dilute solution.

First we shall consider a simple gaseous reaction wherein A atoms react with B atoms to produce AB molecules. The chemists would write the reaction in this fashion:

$$A + B \longrightarrow AB \qquad AB \equiv C \qquad (4\text{–}126)$$

We are calling the molecule AB simply C because of the brevity we will soon need in the subscripts.

We are going to treat these reacting atoms as well as the molecular product as though they were perfect gases, the only deviation being that they react. We define the following list of symbols:

N is the total number of A atoms, including the free ones and those combined in the molecule C.

M is the total number of B atoms, including the free ones and those combined in the molecule C.

R is the number of molecules of $C \equiv AB$.

N_f is the number of free A atoms.

$$N_f = N - R \qquad (4\text{–}127)$$

M_f is the number of free B atoms.

$$M_f = M - R \qquad (4\text{–}128)$$

n_j is the number of A atoms having energy e_j.
m_j is the number of B atoms having energy e'_j.
r_j is the number of C molecules having energy e''_j.

*Reference 16, p. 126, Ref. 4, p. 84, and Ref. 26, pp. 479–503. Also, Ref. 8 in general.

There has been enough discussion in previous sections for the reader to compute the equibrium concentrations A, B, and C by short methods (with some effort), but for clarity, a detailed approach will follow, using the Lagrange method of undetermined multipliers.

The number of ways that n_j atoms having energy e_1, n_2 atoms having energy e_2, n_3 atoms of energy e_3, and so on, can be arranged in an independent localized system is (see Eq. 1–19).

$$W_L = \frac{N!}{\pi n_j!} \qquad (4\text{-}129)$$

but the number of ways in a nonlocalized system is

$$W_A = \frac{W_L}{N!} = \frac{1}{\pi n_j!} \qquad (4\text{-}130a)$$

Similarly,

$$W_B = \frac{1}{\pi m_j!} \qquad (4\text{-}130b)$$

and

$$W_C = \frac{1}{\pi r_j!} \qquad (4\text{-}130c)$$

The combined number of ways is

$$W = W_A W_B W_C = \frac{1}{\pi n_j!\, \pi m_j!\, \pi r_j!} \qquad (4\text{-}131)$$

The logarithm of the number of ways, Stirling's approximation, $\ln n! = n \ln n - n$, being used, is

$$\ln W = -\sum n_j(\ln n_j - 1) - \sum m_j(\ln m_j - 1) - \sum r_j(\ln r_j - 1) \qquad (4\text{-}132)$$

This equation is the first of four equations to be simultaneously satisfied. The other three are

$$\sum n_j + \sum r_j = N \qquad (4\text{-}133a)$$

$$\sum m_j + \sum r_j = M \qquad (4\text{-}133b)$$

$$\sum n_j e_j + \sum m_j e'_j + \sum r_j e''_j = E \qquad (4\text{-}133c)$$

Following the procedure of Sec. 2–6, we now differentiate Eqs. 4–132 and 4–133(a–c), then multiply Eq. 4–133(a) by α_A, 4–133(b) by α_B, and 4–133(c) by β and equate to zero.

$$\sum \ln n_j\, \partial n_j + \sum \ln m_j\, \partial m_j + \sum \ln r_j\, \partial r_j = 0$$

$$\alpha_A \sum \partial n_j + \alpha_A \sum \partial r_j = 0$$

$$\alpha_B \sum \partial m_j + \alpha_B \sum \partial r_j = 0$$

$$\beta \sum e_j\, \partial n_j + \beta \sum e'_j\, \partial m_j + \beta \sum e''_j\, \partial r_j = 0$$

Adding these equations and equating to zero term by term yields three equations.

$$\ln n_j + \alpha_A + \beta e_j = 0$$
$$\ln m_j + \alpha_B + \beta e'_j = 0$$
$$\ln r_j + (\alpha_A + \alpha_B) + \beta e''_j = 0$$

or

$$n_j = e^{-\alpha_A} e^{-\beta e_j} \qquad (4\text{-}134a)$$

$$m_j = e^{-\alpha_B} e^{-\beta e_j'} \qquad (4\text{-}134b)$$

$$r_j = e^{-(\alpha_A + \alpha_B)} e^{-\beta e_j''} \qquad (4\text{-}134c)$$

Substituting these values of n_j, m_j, and r_j into Eqs. 4–133(a–c) in the same manner that was followed in Sec. 2–6, we get

$$n_j = \frac{N_f e^{-e_j/kT}}{Q_n} \qquad (4\text{-}135a)$$

$$m_j = \frac{M_f e^{-e_j'/kT}}{Q_m} \qquad (4\text{-}135b)$$

$$r_j = \frac{R e^{-e_j''/kT}}{Q_r} \qquad (4\text{-}135c)$$

When Eqs. 4–135(a–c) are applied to Eq. 4–132, we find that

$$\ln W = -[\Sigma N_f e^{-e_j/kT} \ln N_f e^{-e_j/kT} + \Sigma M_f e^{-e_j'/kT} \ln M_f e^{-e_j'/kT}$$
$$+ R_j e^{-e_j''/kT} \ln R_j e^{-e_j''/kT}]$$

After some rearranging, this becomes

$$\ln W = -N_f \ln N_f + N_f \ln Q_n + N_f + \frac{E_n}{kT}$$

$$-M_f \ln M_f + M_f \ln Q_m + M_f + \frac{E_m}{kT}$$

$$-R \ln R + R \ln Q_r + R + \frac{E_r}{kT} \qquad (4\text{-}136)$$

Knowing that $E_n + E_m + E_r = E$ and that $N_f \ln N_f - N = \ln N_f!$, we find that Eq. 4–136 is transformed.

$$\ln W = \frac{E}{kT} + N_f \ln Q_n + M_f \ln Q_m + N_r \ln Q_r$$

$$- \ln N_f - \ln M_f - \ln R$$

$$= \frac{E}{kT} + \ln \frac{Q_n^{N_f} Q_m^{M_f} Q_r^{R}}{N_f! \, M_f! \, R!} \qquad (4\text{-}137)$$

$$kT \ln W \equiv TS = E + kT \ln Q_n^{N_f} Q_m^{M_f} Q_r^{R}$$

$$\equiv E - F \qquad (4\text{-}138)$$

central maximum in melting temperature flanked by two eutectics. The lead-tin diagram shown in Fig. 4–15 shows an area *ss* representing a wide range of compositions over which there is complete solid solubility. By connecting the lines *ab* to *de* through *c* we get a loop similar to the one we computed in a previous section (see Fig. 4–9). The point *c* can be identified as a predicted critical temperature T_c, although the dotted part of the curve including *c* is fictitious and is

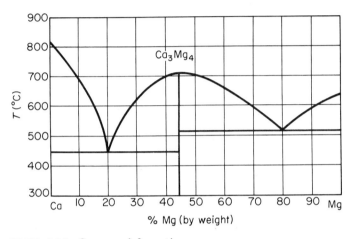

FIGURE **4-14** Compound formation.

FIGURE **4-15** An immiscibility gap penetrating the liquid phase only hypothetically.

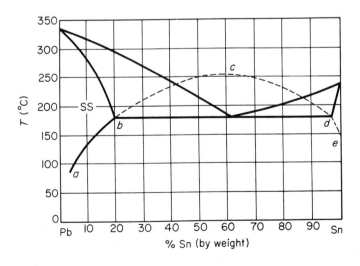

never observed experimentally, because melting occurs first in Pb-Sn alloys. Figure 4–16 shows, by connecting the curve *ab* to *d* through *c*, a sort of hidden compound near 30 weight per cent zinc which is

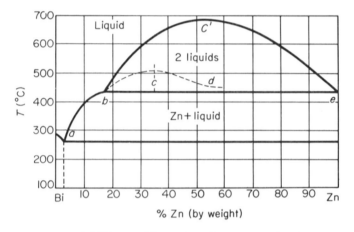

FIGURE **4-16** A hidden melting point of a compound whose formation is prevented by dissolution.

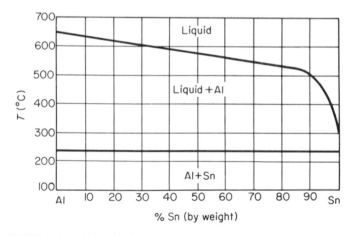

FIGURE **4-17** A lopsided diagram.

interrupted by melting; of equal interest is the observed curve *bc'e* which shows the temperatures above which the liquid metals Bi and Zn are totally miscible, and below which there is a range of compositions wherein liquid zinc can separate out and float on liquid bismuth like benzene on water. The maximum temperature at *c'* is a critical temperature for this immiscibility, and the mathematical treatment is not terribly different from that used for solid solutions in Sec. 4–12.

Let us see if we get an approximate theoretical solution to problems of which Fig. 4–12 is an example. We start the procedure in much the same manner that we did in Sec. 4–12. In general, we will say that we have two kinds of atoms, A atoms and B atoms, totalling N atoms. The fraction of A atoms is $f = N_a/N$ and the fraction of B atoms is $(1 - f) = N_b/N$. The energy required to break an A–A bond is E_{aa} as before, the energy for a B–B bond is E_{bb}, and the energy to break an A–B bond is E_{ab}.

The chance that any atom picked at random in the mixture is an A atom is $C_{a0} = f = N_a/N$ and the chance that a neighboring atom is also an A atom is $C_{0a} = fW$. So the chance that an A atom has an A nearest neighbor is

$$C_{aa} = C_{0a}C_{a0} = f^2 W \qquad (4\text{–}144a)$$

where W is again the coordination number. Similar reasoning predicts that

$$C_{bb} = (1 - f)^2 W \qquad (4\text{–}144b)$$

and

$$C_{ab} = f(1 - f)W \qquad (4\text{–}144c)$$

Then the total numbers of bonds of the three types are

$$N_{aa} = NC_{aa} = \frac{N}{2} Wf^2 \qquad (4\text{–}145a)$$

$$N_{bb} = NC_{bb} = \frac{N}{2} W(1 - f)^2 \qquad (4\text{–}145b)$$

$$N_{ab} = NC_{ab} = \frac{N}{2} Wf(1 - f) \qquad (4\text{–}145c)$$

The energy of such a solid system at absolute zero is

$$E_{S0} = N_{aa}E_{aa} + N_{bb}E_{bb} + N_{ab}E_{ab}$$

$$= \frac{N}{2} W[f^2 E_{aa} + (1 - f)^2 E_{bb} + f(1 - f)E_{ab}]$$

$$= \frac{N}{2} W\left\{ fE_{aa} + (1 - f)E_{bb} - 2f(1 - f)\left[E_{ab} - \frac{E_{aa} + E_{bb}}{2} \right] \right\} \qquad (4\text{–}146)$$

It will be remembered that when E_{ab} is less than the mean $(E_{aa} + E_{bb})/2$, then the atomic bonds A–A and B–B were inclined to form at the expense of AB bonds, and the pure metals were inclined to separate, as illustrated in Figs. 4–9 and 4–11(a). At the present moment, with our minds on Fig. 4–12 we wish to let $E_{ab} = (E_{aa} + E_{bb})/2$ so that Eq.

4–146 becomes

$$E_{S0} = \frac{NW}{2}\{fE_{aa} + (1-f)E_{bb}\} \tag{4-147}$$

We know that $NW/2E_{aa}$ is really the heat of sublimation of pure A at absolute zero into a vacuum, and similarly with regard to B. So Eq. 4–147 can be written

$$E_{S0} = f\,\Delta E_{a0} + (1-f)\,\Delta E_{b0} \tag{4-148}$$

It must be remembered that ΔE_{a0} and ΔE_{b0} are negative quantities and contribute to the free energy F, causing it to have a greater negative value at $0°K$ than at any other temperature. Since stability increases as F goes more negative, the perfect solid state is most stable at absolute zero. At higher temperatures another term must be added, $\int C_p\,dT$, where the heat capacity C_p must be determined by experiment.

$$E_{ST} = f\,\Delta E_{a0} + (1-f)\Delta E_{b0} + \int_0^T C_p\,dT \tag{4-149}$$

The last term is a positive quantity and causes E_{ST} to be less negative. When E_{S0} in Eq. 4–148 is plotted against f, a straight line aa' is obtained, as shown in Fig. 4–18. Also, it is to be noticed that we have over-simplified the heat capacity term and have not prorated it as we should for the general case:

$$C_p(f) = C_{pa}f + C_{pb}(1-f) \tag{4-150}$$

where C_{pa} and C_{pb} are the heat capacities of the pure substances. But for convenience we have assumed that $C_{pa} = C_{pb}$. Thus when E_{ST} in Eq. 4–149 is plotted against f we get a set of *parallel* lines, shown in Fig. 4–18.

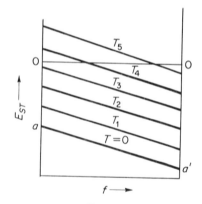

FIGURE **4-18** The straight lines obtained by plotting the energy E_{ST} of the solid state at various temperatures against the composition expressed as a fraction f. These straight lines are obtained only when $E_{ab} = (E_{aa} + E_{bb})/2$.

Before computing the free energy F of the solid, we need to compute the entropy in order to combine it with Eq. 4–150 to get

$$F_{ST} = E_{ST} - TS_{ST} \tag{4-151}$$

Similar to Eq. 4–73, the entropy of mixing is

$$S_{S0} = -kN[f\ln f + (1-f)\ln(1-f)] \tag{4-152}$$

At higher temperatures a term must be added to this.

$$\int \frac{C_p}{T}\,dT \quad \text{or} \quad \int C_p\,d\ln T$$

so that

$$S_{ST} = -kN[f\ln f + (1 + f)\ln(1 - f) + \int_0^T C_p\, d\ln T \quad (4\text{-}153)$$

Now, substituting Eqs. 4–150 and 4–153 into Eq. 4–151 gives the free energy of the solid mixture at temperature T:

$$F_{ST} = f\,\Delta E_{a0} + (1 - f)\,\Delta E_{b0} + \int_0^T C_p\, dT$$

$$- NkT[f\ln f + (1 - f)\ln(1 - f) + T\int_0^T C_p\, d\ln T \quad (4\text{-}154)$$

In plotting these curves we find that from Eq. 4–152 the $-S_{S0}$ curve is a "sagging rope," as shown in Fig. 4–19, but for higher temperatures the $-S_{ST}$ curves are raised. When the negatives of the S_{ST} curves are multiplied by T and added to the E_{ST} curves of Fig. 4–18, as dictated by Eq. 4–154, a series of curves is obtained, as shown in Fig. 4–20.

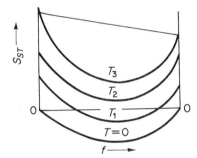

FIGURE **4-19** The "sagging rope" type of curves obtained when the entropy S_{ST} is plotted against f for various temperatures (see Eq. 4–159).

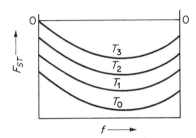

FIGURE **4-20** The plot of F_{ST} (see Eq. 4–151) of the solid $F_{ST} = E_{ST} - TS_{ST}$ at various temperatures according to the more detailed Eq. 4–154.

With all this in mind, we save Eq. 4–154 and Fig. 4–20 for a comparison of an analogous computation of free energy F_{LT} for the mixture in the liquid state. The energy of the liquid at absolute zero is the same as that of the solid, except that (since the atoms are in an amorphous configuration) they are, on the average, farther apart and also contain more holes or vacancies. The energy to change from the crystalline to the amorphous structure is the heat of fusion at absolute zero.

$$E_{L0} = E_{S0} - \Delta E_M = E_{S0} - [f\,\Delta E_{Ma} + (1 - f)E_{Mb}] \quad (4\text{-}155)$$

where ΔE_{Ma} and ΔE_{Mb} are the heats of fusion of A and B, respectively. From Eq. 4–148 we get

$$E_{L0} = f\,\Delta E_{a0} + (1-f)\,\Delta E_{b0} - [f_0\,\Delta E_{Ma} + (1-f)\,\Delta E_{Mb}] \qquad (4\text{–}156)$$

At a higher temperature

$$E_{LT} = f(\Delta E_{a0} - \Delta E_{Ma}) + (1-f)(\Delta E_{b0} - \Delta E_{Mb}) + \int_0^T c_p\,dT \qquad (4\text{–}157)$$

The big difference between the entropies of the solid and liquid states is the entropy of conversion from solid to liquid which is assumed to be independent of temperature and can be measured at the melting point as $\Delta S_{Ma} = \Delta E_{Ma}/T_M$ (as well as by other methods).*

$$S_{L0} = -kN\left[f\ln f - (1-f)\ln(1-f) + f\frac{\Delta E_{Ma}}{T_{Ma}} + (1-f)\frac{\Delta E_{Mb}}{T_{Mb}}\right]$$
$$(4\text{–}158)$$

where T_{Ma} is the melting temperature of A. At higher temperatures

$$S_{LT} = -kN\left[f\ln f + (1-f)\ln(1-f) + f\frac{\Delta E_{Ma}}{T_{Ma}}\right.$$
$$\left. +(1-f)\frac{\Delta E_{Mb}}{T_{Mb}} + \int_0^T C_p\,d\ln T\right] \qquad (4\text{–}159)$$

The graph of S_{LT} against f at various values of T is again a series of "sagging ropes" similar to those in Fig. 4–19, except that they are at higher levels because of the terms, $f\,\Delta E_{Ma}/T_{Ma}$ and $(1-f)\,\Delta E_{Mb}/T_{Mb}$.

Combining Eqs. 4–157 and 4–159 according to Eq. 4–151 gives

$$F_{LT} = f[\Delta E_{a0} - \Delta E_{Ma}] + (1-f)[\Delta E_{b0} - \Delta E_{Mb}] + \int_0^T C_p\,dT$$
$$+ kN\left[f\ln f + (1-f)\ln(1-f)\right] + T\left[f\frac{\Delta E_{Ma}}{T_{Ma}} + (1-f)\frac{\Delta E_{Mb}}{T_{Mb}}\right]$$
$$(4\text{–}160)$$

A graph of Eq. 4–160 is similar to that of Eq. 4–154 shown in Fig. 4–20 except that it starts higher at $T = 0$, indicating that at low temperatures the solid is the most stable phase at all compositions. A second difference is that the F_{LT} curves do not rise as fast with temperature as the F_{ST} curves. In fact, the F_{ST} curves overtake and pass the F_{LT} curves, as shown in Figs. 4–21 (a–e).

Let us illustrate these things with actual numbers, using the data in Table 4–2.

$$\Delta E_{b0} = 1.5\,\Delta E_{a0}, \qquad \Delta E_{Mb} = 2\,\Delta E_{Ma}, \qquad T_{Mb} = 2T_{Ma}, \qquad \Delta E_{Mb} = \Delta E_{Ma}$$

*See Ref. 27.

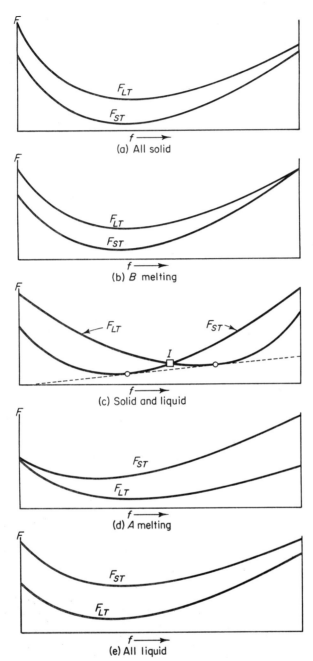

FIGURE 4-21 A series of curves of the free energy (Helmholtz) plotted against f at five different temperatures. Curves (b) and (d) are at the melting points of the pure components B and A, respectively. Note that the free energy of the solid overtakes that of the liquid until at the higher temperatures selected for (e) the free energy of the liquid is lower than that of the solid at all compositions.

Table 4-2 BASIC DATA

	ΔE_S	ΔE_M	T_M	$\dfrac{\Delta E_M}{T_M} = \Delta S_M$	C_p
A	40,000 cal	2,500	900°K	2.77	7
B	60,000	5,000	1,800	2.77	7

Also assume $C_p = 7.0$ calories per degree is the same for A and B in both solid and liquid states. Then

$$\int C_p \, dT = 7T$$

and

$$\int \frac{C_p}{T} \, dT = 7 \ln T$$

Equation 4–154 can be expressed

$$F_{ST} = -40,000[f + 1.5(1 - f)] + 7T$$
$$-2T[f \ln f + (1 - f) \ln (1 - f)] - 7 \ln T \qquad \text{(4–161a)}$$

which can split up for future reference as follows:

$$F_{ST} = A + B + C + D \qquad \text{(4–161b)}$$

where A, B, C, and D are the first, second, third, and fourth terms in Eq. 4–161(a). For actual calculations, Tables 4–3—4–6 are convenient.

Table 4-3 COMPILATION OF $A = 40,000[f + 1.5(1 - f)]$

f	$1 - f$	$1.5(1 - f)$	$f + 1.5(1 - f)$	$40,000[f + 1.5(1 - f)] = A$
0.0	1	1.5	1.5	60,000
0.05	0.95	1.42	1.475	59,000
0.1	0.90	1.35	1.45	58,000
0.2	0.80	1.20	1.40	56,000
0.3	0.70	1.05	1.35	54,000
0.4	0.60	0.90	1.30	52,000
0.5	0.50	0.75	1.25	50,000
0.6	0.40	0.60	1.20	48,000
0.7	0.30	0.45	1.15	46,000
0.8	0.20	0.30	1.10	44,000
0.9	0.10	0.15	1.05	42,000
0.95	0.05	0.075	1.025	41,000
1.00	0.00	0	1.00	40,000

Table 4-4 COMPILATION OF $B = 7T$

T	$7T$	T	$7T$
900	6300	1400	9888
1000	7000	1600	11,200
1200	8400	1800	12,600

Table 4-5 COMPUTATION OF $C = 2T\left[f \ln \dfrac{1}{f} + (1 - f) \ln \dfrac{1}{1-f} \right] = 2TY$

f	y	$T = 900$	$T = 1000$	$T = 1200$	$T = 1400$	$T = 1600$	$T = 1800$
0	0	0	0	0	0	0	0
0.05	0.184	332	368	441	516	580	662
0.10	0.322	535	644	773	900	1030	1152
0.20	0.484	870	965	1160	1340	1565	1740
0.30	0.599	1075	1195	1435	1670	1910	2150
0.40	0.668	1200	1330	1580	1870	2130	2400
0.50	0.69	1240	1380	1655	1930	2210	2480
0.60	0.688	1200	1330	1580	1870	2130	2400
0.70	0.599	1075	1195	1435	1670	1910	2150
0.80	0.484	870	965	1160	1340	1565	1740
0.90	0.322	535	644	773	900	1030	1152
0.95	0.184	332	368	414	516	580	662
1.00	0	0	0	0	0	0	0

Table 4-6 COMPUTATION OF $D = 7 \ln T$

T	$7 \ln T$	T	$7 \ln T$
900	47.6	1400	50.8
1000	48.4	1600	51.5
1200	49.5	1800	52.4

Now following Eq. 4-161(a) the value of F_{ST} at 1800°C and $f = 0.5$ is

$$F_S(900°) = -50,000 + 12,600 - 2,480 - 52.4 \qquad (4\text{-}162)$$

One can see from Eq. 4-161(b) and Table 4-3 that A is a very large number compared to the rest of the terms, and a plot of A as a function of f is a straight line between 40,000 calories and 60,000 and has no minimum, although it is f sensitive (see Fig. 4-22). Terms B and D are temperature dependent, but not f dependent; they act only to elevate the curve of F_{nsf} with an increase in temperature. The only term that contributes to the curvature of the $F - f$ curve is the C term (see Fig. 4–23). The dip in the curve at $T = 900°K$ and $f = 0.5$ (where the dip is the greatest) is only 2480 out of 50,000, and actual graphs showing these great latitudes are not as impressive as the schematic graphs shown in Fig. 4–21(a–e). A much more practical thing to deal with is F_{ST}^*, which is defined as the change in F_S on mixing.

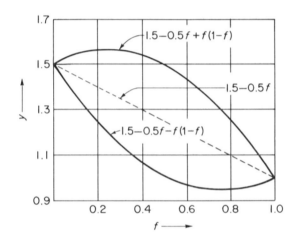

FIGURE **4-22** If in Eq. 4–146 $E_{ab} = (E_{aa} + E_{bb})/2$ and $E_{aa} = 1.5E_{bb}$, then the variable term to be multiplied by $N/2W$ is $1.5 - 0.5f$ shown in the fourth column of Table 4–3. When it is plotted against f, we get the straight dotted line in this figure the same as the line aa' in Fig. 4–18. However, when $E_{ab} - (E_{aa} + E_{bb})/2 = 0.5E_{bb}$ we get the upper curve; if $E_{ab} - E_{aa} + E_{bb} = -0.5E_{bb}$, we get the lower curve for the factor. (However, we must remember that the E values are negative.)

$$F_{ST}^* = F_{ST} - A - B - D = C = RT[f \ln f + (1 - f) \ln (1 - f)]$$

$$(4\text{--}163)$$

A graph of C/RT against f is shown in Fig. 4–23.
For the liquid state, Eq. 4–160 can be rewritten.

$$F_{LT} = f \Delta E_{a0} + (1 - f) \Delta E_{b0} + \int_0^T C_p \, dT$$

$$- R\left[f \ln \frac{1}{f} + (1 - f) \ln \frac{1}{1 - f}\right] + C_p \, d \ln T$$

$$+ [f \Delta E_{Ma} + (1 - f) \Delta E_{Mb}] + T\left[f \frac{\Delta E_{Ma}}{T_{Ma}} + (1 - f) \frac{\Delta E_{Ma}}{T_{Mb}}\right]$$

$$= A + B + C + D + \mathscr{E} + \mathscr{F}$$

$$(4\text{--}164)$$

of which the first four terms are identical to Eq. 4–154. Therefore,

$$F_{LT} = F_{ST} + [f\,\Delta E_{Ma} + (1 - f)\,\Delta E_{Mb}]$$
$$+ T\left[f\frac{\Delta E_{Ma}}{T_{Ma}} + (1 - f)\frac{\Delta E_{Mb}}{T_{Mb}}\right]$$
$$= F_{ST} + \mathscr{E} + \mathscr{F} \qquad\qquad (4\text{–}165)$$

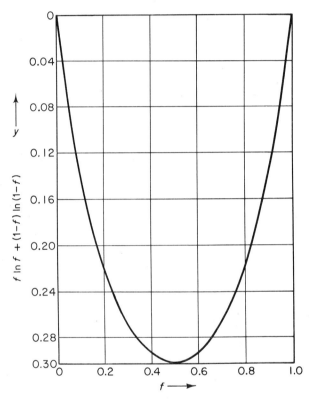

FIGURE **4-23**   Indicating how, in the present case, the free energy of mixing
is a minimum at $f = 0.5$.

Since the $\mathscr{F}$ term contains $\Delta E_{Ma}/T_{Ma}$ and $\Delta E_{Mb}/T_{Mb}$ which, according
to Table 4–2 are equal to one another, i.e., $\Delta S_M = 2.77$, it is not a
function of f but only of T.

$$\mathscr{F} = 2.77T \qquad\qquad (4\text{–}166a)$$

The $\mathscr{E}$ term in Eq. 4–165 is (see Table 4–7)

$$\mathscr{E} = [f\,2500 + (1 - f)5000]$$
$$= 2500[f + 2(1 - f)] = 2500(2 - f) \qquad\qquad (4\text{–}166b)$$

Now Eq. 4–165 becomes

$$F_{LT} = F_{ST} - 2500(2 - f) + 2.77T$$

Notice that the $\mathscr{E}$ term in Eq. 4–165 is another straight line but it has a different slope from the term A in Eqs. 4–161(a–b). Therefore, $\mathscr{E}$ and $\mathscr{F}$ must be retained for the objective we have in mind. The objective is to determine a comparison in the change in free energy of mixing of solid and liquid, that is, F_x^* given in Eq. 4–163,

$$F_{ST}^* = -RT\left[f\ln\frac{1}{f} + (1 - f)\ln\frac{1}{1 - f}\right] \qquad (4\text{–}167)$$

and

$$F_{LT} = F_{ST}^* + 2500(2 - f) - 2.77T \qquad (4\text{–}168)$$

FIGURE **4-24** The graphs of F_{ST}^*, according to Eq. 4–167, and F_{SL}^*, Eq. 4–168, from the data of Tables 4–7 and 4–8. The free energy changes for the solid state are in solid lines, and those for the liquid are in dotted lines. The points of intersection for the same temperature are marked as squares, and the points of tangency are circles.

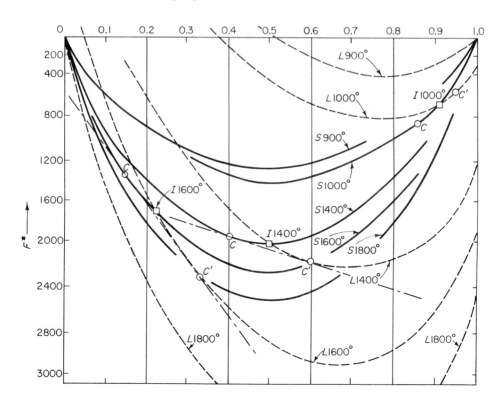

Tables 4–7 and 4–8 were used to make the graphs in Fig. 4–24, and from this figure the method of tangents was used to draw Fig. 4–25.

Table 4-7 COMPUTATION OF $\mathscr{E} - \mathscr{F}$ FROM EQS. 4-166(a-b)

		$\mathscr{E}$			$\mathscr{E} - \mathscr{F}$			
			$T=900°$	$100°$	$1200°$	$1400°$	$1600°$	$1800°$
f	$2-f$	$2500(2-f)$	2500	2770	3300	3750	4400	5000←$2.77T=F$
0	2	5000	2500	2230	1700	1250	600	000
0.05	1.95	4875	2375	2105	1575	1125	475	−125
0.10	1.9	4750	2250	1980	1450	1000	350	−250
0.20	1.8	4500	2000	1730	1200	750	100	−500
0.30	1.7	4250	1750	1480	950	500	−150	−750
0.40	1.6	4000	1500	1230	700	250	−400	−1000
0.50	1.5	3750	1250	980	450	00	−650	−1250
0.60	1.4	3500	1000	830	200	−250	−900	−1500
0.70	1.3	3250	750	480	−50	−500	−1150	−1750
0.80	1.2	3000	500	230	−300	−750	−1400	−2000
0.90	1.1	2750	250	−20	−550	−1000	−1650	−2250
0.95	1.05	2625	125	−145	−675	−1125	−1775	−2375
1.00	1.00	2500	000	−270	−800	−1250	−1900	−2500

Table 4-8 COMPUTATION OF F_L^*

f	$T=900°$	$T=100°$	$+1200°$	$1400°$	$1600°$	$1800°$
0	+2500	+2230	+1700	+1250	+600	00
0.05	+2042	+1737	+1134	+609	−105	−787
0.10	+1715	+1336	+677	+100	−680	−1302
0.20	+1130	+765	+40	−590	−1465	−2240
0.30	+675	+285	−485	−1170	−2060	−2900
0.40	+300	−100	−880	−1620	−2530	−3400
0.50	+10	−400	−1205	−1930	−2860	−3730
0.60	−200	−500	−1380	−2120	−3030	−3900
0.70	−325	−715	−1485	−2170	−3060	−3900
0.80	−370	−735	−1460	−2090	−2965	−3740
0.90	−285	−664	−1323	−1900	−2680	−3400
0.95	−207	−513	−1089	−1641	−2255	−3037
1.00	0	−270	−800	−1250	−1900	−2500

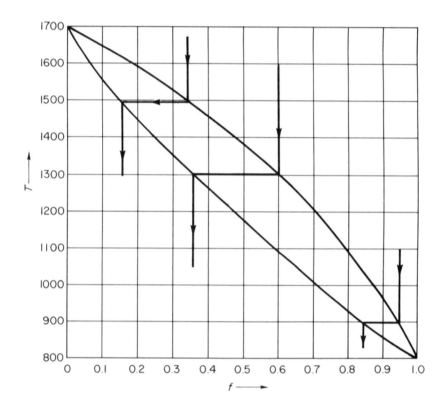

FIGURE **4-25** Showing the use of the data taken from Fig. 4-24; i.e., the temperatures T and the f values from the common tangencies.

PROBLEMS

1. (a) Knowing that for vibration

$$e_j = (j + \tfrac{1}{2})hv$$

can you show that the energy difference between two adjacent levels is

$$\Delta e = hv$$

for all j's?

(b) Knowing that the energy of rotation for a diatomic molecule is

$$e_j = \frac{h^2}{8\pi^2 I} j(j + 1)$$

can you show that the frequency emitted in dropping from an energy level e_j to the next lowest level is

$$v = \frac{h^2 2j}{8\pi^2 I}$$

2. (a) If HCl is known from spectroscopic data to rotate with a frequency of 62.04×10^{10} cycles per second, compute the moment of inertia from the equation

$$\nu_1 = \frac{2h}{8\pi^2 I}$$

(b) Compare this frequency 62.04×10^{10} with the frequency of vibration of some of the metals as computed in Problem 11 in Chapter 3; and to that of HCl in Problem 10 in Chapter 3.

(c) Knowing that

$$I = \mu r^2$$

and knowing the masses of the hydrogen atom and chlorine atom, compute the distance r between atoms. Do you get 1.29×10^{-8} centimeters or 1.29 Angstrom units? Does this look reasonable?

3. (a) You have 6.02×10^{23} hydrogen atoms encapsulated so that each atom is in a cube, one centimeter on a side heated to one million degrees, and all the cubes arranged side to side so that six sides of each are touching its neighbors' sides (except at the boundaries, of course) so that energy can cross the boundaries but the atoms can not; can you compute the partition function Q?

(b) Remove the boundaries in (a) and compute the new value of Q.

4. (a) Compute the partition function of the "flat gas" described in Sec. 4–6.

(b) Compute the Helmholtz free energy of the "flat gas" described in Sec. 4–6.

5. Explore the similarities between the Morse function

$$e(r) = e_0(1 - e^{-\beta(r-r_0)})^2$$

and a function used by Lennard-Jones and Grüneisen,

$$e(r) = \frac{e_0}{m-n}\left[-m\left(\frac{r_0}{r}\right)^n + n\left(\frac{r_0}{r}\right)^m\right]$$

where e_0 has the same meaning in both equations and r_0 means the equilibrium distance in both equations, whereas β, m, and n are constants with m larger than n.

6. (a) Taking the equation for Helmholtz's free energy of mixing (Eq. 4–73a)

$$\Delta F = \frac{NW}{2}f(1-f)[2E_{AB} - E_{AA} - E_{BB}]$$
$$+ TkN[f\ln f + (1-f)\ln(1-f)]$$

plot a curve at $T = 0$ for the case (for convenience, let $NW/2 = \frac{1}{2}$ and choose your own values of E_{AA} and E_{BB} and remember that these are negative numbers)

$$E_{AB} = \frac{E_{AA} - E_{BB}}{2}$$

(b) Plot a curve at $T = 0$ for the case

$$E_{AB} = \frac{1}{2} \frac{(E_{AA} - E_{BB})}{2}$$

(c) Plot a curve at $T = 0$ for the case

$$E_{AB} = 2\left(\frac{E_{AA} - E_{BB}}{2}\right)$$

(d) For each of the three cases in Prob. 6(a–c) and still letting $NW/2 = \frac{1}{2}$, plot curves where $TkN = \frac{1}{2}$, 1, 2, and 4.

(e) Substitute your chossn values of E_{AA} and E_{BB} and the convenient values $NW/2 = \frac{1}{2}$ and $TkN = 2$ into Eq. 4–73(a) and differentiate with respect to f to get the minima in one of the curves of Prob. 6(d).

(f) Which of the three conditions for the values of E_{AB} as given in Prob. 6(a–c) predict that there will be a separation of phases?

(g) Differentiate Eq. 4–73(a) twice with respect to temperature and predict the highest temperature at which two phases can exist.

7. (a) There has long been used a laboratory method of determining the entropy of a substance at any temperature. It compreses measuring the amount of heat required to raise the temperature of that substance in stages from $0°K$ and applying the following equation:

$$S = \int_0^{T_1} C_p \, d \ln T + \frac{\Delta H_1}{T} + \int_{T_1}^{T_2} C_p \, d \ln T + \frac{\Delta H_2}{T} \cdots$$

where T_1, T_2, etc. are temperatures of phase transitions and ΔH_1, ΔH_2, etc. are the enthalpies of the transitions. The data in the table were obtained for HCl. Calculate from this table the entropy of HCl at the

Temperature Interval	Entropy Increase ΔS	Temperature of Transition	Heat of Transition
0–16°K	0.03		
16°–98.36	7.06		
Solid-solid transformation		98.36(SS)	284.3
98.36–158.91	5.05		
Melting		158.91(SL)	476.0
158.91–188.07	2.36		
Boiling		188.07(LG)	3860

boiling point. The entropies are in calories per degree per mole, and the heats of transition are in calories per mole.

(b) The spectroscopists get 41.2 calories per mole per degree for HCl at the boiling point. How does your result compare?

(c) Outline a procedure you would take if you had complete spectroscopic data at hand and were asked to compute the entropy of a diatomic gas such as HCl at 100°C. (Remember that the symmetry number of HCl is unity.)

8. (a) Using Eq. 4–110 for the equilibrium number of vacancies in a metal,

$$n = N\left(\frac{\nu}{\nu'}\right)^{3W} e^{-\mathscr{E}/kT}$$

and supposing that

$$\left(\frac{\nu}{\nu'}\right) = \sqrt{\frac{W}{W-1}} = \sqrt{\frac{12}{11}} = \sqrt{1.1} = 1.05$$

for a face-centered structure, i.e., $W = 12$, and that $E = 20,000/N$ so that

$$\frac{\mathscr{E}}{kT} = \frac{20,000}{RT} = \frac{20,000}{2T}$$

compute the number of vacancies per mole at 2000°K and at 223°K.

(b) If a piece of metal were soaked at 2000°K until it attained the equilibrium number of holes and its dimensions measured, then cooled slowly to room temperature, what further percentage volume shrinkage would you expect?

9. (a) The vapor pressure of solid* cadmium is given in the table as follows (these data are questionable):

Temperature °C	Pressure in mm Hg
138.2	1.0×10^{-7}
168.7	2.2×10^{-5}
178.2	5.11×10^{-5}
197.7	2.56×10^{-4}
208.8	4.35×10^{-4}
220.7	8.99×10^{-4}
229.5	1.65×10^{-3}
259.4	7.80×10^{-3}

*See Y. G. Aston, *Treatise on Physical Chemistry*, I, p. 513 (Princeton, N. J.: Van Nostrand, 1942). For a good treatment of vapor pressure with methods and tables, see A. N. Nesmeyanov, *Vapor Pressure of the Chemical Elements* (Amsterdam: Elsevier Publishing Company, 1963).

Calculate, using graphs, the heat of sublimation.

(b) The vapor pressures of liquid cadmium are:

Temperature °C	Pressure in mm Hg
503	15
549	32
583	60
645	159.5
698	332
756	672
804	1131
836	1536

Calculate from graphs the heat of vaporization.

(c) If you subtract the heat of vaporization from the heat of sublimation, would you expect to get the heat of fusion? The literature reports the heat of fusion of cadmium to be about 1460 calories.

10. (a) The following data were collected on mixtures of gaseous hydrogen and iodine:

Initial Concentrations		Final Concentrations
of Hydrogen	of Iodine	of Hydrogen Iodide at Equilibrium
2.94	8.10	5.64
5.30	7.94	9.40
9.27	8.07	13.47
14.44	8.12	14.93
27.53	8.02	15.54
33.10	7.89	15.40

From these data calculate the equilibrium constant for the six mixtures and see how it varies.

(b) Calculate the free energy change of the reaction.

11. From the study of this chapter, can you suggest other aspects of binary phase diagrams which you think could be subjected to statistical mechanics?

INDEX